Praise for *"A Beekeeper's Diary"*

2021 Independent Book Publishers Home and Garden Bronze Winner

"What a delightful book! It is so comprehensive, it makes me feel as though I could raise bees myself! The structure, pacing, and organization are perfect. You take the reader's hand and guide them, step-by-step, on how to go about ~~cre~~*ating a hive and taking care of the bees in a way that is easy to understand. I learned so much . . . ."*

— **WRITER'S DIGEST REVIEW**

October 2021

"The Queen of organizing is back. This time Charlotte Ekker Wiggins has ~~cre~~*ated a book full of information to help organize the 'chaotic myriad of basic* ~~de~~*cisions' we all face in our apiaries. Filled with wonderful charts and practical* ~~i~~*nformation, it is meant to be a guide to helping us manage our bees smoothly from month to month. With a fun, easy-to-read style, Ekker Wiggins presents all the basics needed to keep hives healthy and happy . . . . What do you expect from a person who does a TED Talk in a bee suit? She even tells us how to prevent hangovers with honey. Did I mention this woman is FUN?"*

— **Carol Hrusovszky**

AMERICAN BEE JOURNAL, July 2021

"Just a note to say how much I've enjoyed your book 'A Beekeepers Diary.' I've been a beekeeper for 7 years and like many have become a bee nerd in my book collecting. I've never been able to recommend just one book to new beekeepers and now I can!"

— **Karen Veleta**

June 26, 2021

"For those of you just starting out with honey bees, the process may seem daunting. Everything that looked simple on a video becomes immensely complicated when you try it alone. And scary, too.

Now, help is available. Missouri beekeeper Charlotte Ekker Wiggins has published a new book titled A Beekeeper's Diary: Self Guide to Keeping Bees. Part instruction manual, part workbook, and part diary, the book is filled with useful tidbits to get you started . . . .

Whereas many beginner books simply tell you what to buy, this book is filled with insider tips like how to wash your bee suit, how to light your smoker, and how to cook with honey. It even contains a hive inspection guide and a month by-month to-do list.

Because she is a passionate gardener, Charlotte provides much information the plants bees love. Too often, beginning beekeepers are overly focused on bees and don't pay enough attention to their environment, a place that needs be filled with the right type of flowers. . . .When you become aware of your local flora and when it blooms, beekeeping can be much more fun . . ."

— Rusty Burlew

Honey Bee Suite April 2021 | www.honeybeesuite.com/book-review-a-beekeepers-diary

". . . This is a great book for a beginning beekeeper as a supplement to a local bee class . . . . Every beginning beekeeping book advises beekeepers to take notes and keep records on their bees, the weather, nectar flows, etc. This is a book that actually supports the need for record keeping. The 'Good to Know' and 'Good Tip' sections get to the important questions and information for each section. As the majority of beekeepers are older folks wearing bifocals the big print is greatly appreciated . . . . The book is a great overview of beekeeping, with a good reading list for in-depth topics once you are hooked as a beekeeper. There is so much to learn about bees, and this book is a great place to start."

— Michele Colopy

Executive Director, LEAD for Pollinators, Inc., beekeeper and D.S. Wolf, honey extracting assistant.

March 2021 Amazon Review

A BEEKEEPER'S DIARY

SELF GUIDE TO KEEPING BEES

SECOND EDITION

Charlotte Ekker Wiggins

Great Plains
Master Beekeeping
Approved Course

A Beekeeper's Diary: Self Guide to Keeping Bees, Second Edition

All photos by, and property of the author, unless otherwise identified.

Printed in the United States of America

First Printing, 2021
Second Edition with Index, December 2021

ISBN: 978-1-7357319-0-2 (Trade Paperback)
ISBN: 978-1-7357319-2-6 (Trade Paperback, 2nd Edition)
ISBN: 978-1-7357319-1-9 (Print Replica eBook)
ISBN: 978-1-7357319-4-0 (Print Replica eBook, 2nd Edition)

Library of Congress Control Number: 2020922578

Published by: Charlotte Ekker Wiggins, LLC | Rolla, MO | CharlotteEkkerWiggins.com

For more information contact: 4charlottewiggins@gmail.com

Cover Illustration: J. Tupper
Cover Design and Interior Formatting: Becky's Graphic Design®, LLC

ON THE COVER:

Blackberries blooming in Missouri mark the beginning of the honey bees, and beekeepers, busiest season. Plants entice pollinators with nectar so bees will carry pollen from one plant to another one, helping the plants reproduce. **Can you identify the different jobs the worker bees are doing?** *(Answers later in the diary)*

Dedication

To the women who inspired the names of my first honey bee queens: **Gertrude**, named after my mother, and **Mildred,** named after my grandmother.

Both women faced adversity with strength, grace and determination. They both, in their own way, also encouraged me to discover, and continuously renew, my awe in the magic that unfolds every day in our gardens.

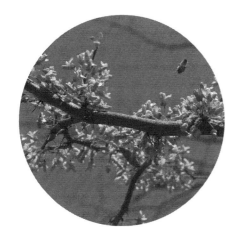

*Missouri's native Eastern Redbuds (Cercis canadensis) in Bluebird Gardens, my Missouri limestone hillside apiary in early spring. Eastern **Redbuds are excellent bee food.** They are also delicious in salads!*

Acknowledgments

Hugs to Rolla Bee Club's Planning Group David Draker, Tom Miller, Jessie Scrivner Gunn and Lorri Thurman, your continued interest and participation makes our club interesting, educational and deliciously fun.

Big bear hug to my "big brother" and bee buddy David Draker, who volunteered in 2014 to go on this beekeeping adventure, and to his wife Gina. They are both still with me. Even when I lose my way. And forget to take my bee antennae headband off before our meetings...

A virtual plant on sale for my gardening buddy Tom Miller, who learns something new from every book that he reads and speaker that he hears. He is so willing to share, unless it's about plants on sale. And he valiantly tries to keep David in line.

A deep hive body full of brood to Gregg Hitchings, Teresa Campbell, Sharon Contini and to Gregg's charming wife Thea for the laughs when we run into each other. With or without Gregg!

A large box of coloring pens to my wonderful illustrator J. Tupper, who now keeps a supply of virtual honey bees at the ready to invite to my book covers. In this edition, meet Queen Begonia again as well as those mischievous drones doing what male bees do second best.

Special thanks and a **bushel of apples** to Becky Bayne and team at Becky's Graphic Design®, LLC for bringing all of the book elements together so professionally. BeckysGraphicDesign.com.

A bottle of honey each to my younger brothers Steve and David who let me go on and on, without interruption, about my bees. Hope you've enjoyed your little cat naps and no - oh, brother, your honey is not better than your other brother's honey.

Contents

A NOTE FROM
Beekeeper Charlotte

I was on my own when I started to keep bees in 2010. This diary is the kind of book that would have helped me when I started. The diary organizes the chaotic myriad of basic decisions beginning beekeepers face. Knowing what is recommended as starting equipment and what options you have when making the decisions makes the learning curve more manageable. It's also kinder on your wallet.

This is also the type of guide that will **come in handy in a physically distancing world because of COVID-19.** Beginning beekeepers look to, and depend on, more experienced beekeepers for advice and guidance. Getting information up close in a world that encourages physical distancing is more than a challenge; these instructions will **fill the gap between** what you read and watch, and **how to actually do it** without someone being there to show you.

The diary can be used with beginning beekeeping classes as well as **Great Plains Master Beekeeping Program** classes certified through the University of Nebraska at Lincoln. I used their beginning beekeeper apprentice level learning objectives to ensure we were including the most up-to-date scientifically based recommended best management practices.

Taking classes is an excellent way to get introduced into what it takes to keep honey bees. It also provides you with a foundation for successful beekeeping as well as further studies if you choose to pursue master beekeeping certification.

You are excited and can't wait to get started? Start by reading through the whole diary to get a sense of what you need to do. Also determine what plants are growing within 2 miles of where you plan to place hives. Make sure your bees will have a continuous supply of blooming flowers that will support them through the blooming season, which in general falls between 74°F and 86°F.

So what do bees eat? Honey bees are the world's leading pollinators, responsible for pollinating one out of every three bites of healthy food we eat. Fruits, vegetables, nuts and seeds are all courtesy of nature's little match makers. Honey bees move pollen from one plant to the next, ensuring the plant's survival. Honey bees are also part of the larger insect population currently threatened by overuse of pesticides, poor nutrition, pathogens, parasites and poor management. It was estimated February 2019 that 40% of the world's insect populations could become extinct in the next decade. **These insects are the foundation of our food supply.**

If you decide not to keep bees, that's ok, too. Not everyone is cut out to be a beekeeper. Your interest in honey bees and the rest of the pollinators can be addressed by planting more flowers and less turf grass, and not using pesticides. You will find "Beekeeping: Why Bugs Matter" in my April 2019 TEDx talk here: **bit.ly/bee-ted-talk**

Also find your closest bee club. You will be more successful being a part of a local beekeeping community. The challenges include:

- It's a steep learning curve; no two beekeeping years are the same.
- It's expensive.
- There are no guarantees.

Remember you are keeping honey bees, not telling bees what to do. The first few years you will learn how to "read your bees" and develop an understanding of what they are doing and why. If you are patient and observant, they will be excellent teachers.

After 40 years of gardening and 11 years of keeping honey bees myself, I can assure you it will be **one of the more exciting, amazing, at times frustrating and heart-breaking, adventures in your life. And it's happening right in your very own backyard.**

Are you ready to take a deeper look at these teeny tiny marvelous creatures?

~ *Charlotte*

*"From working in my apiary, introducing friends to my girls, demonstrating beekeeping techniques at our local bee club and lecturing on planting for pollinators, beekeeping is a **fascinating lifelong hobby!**"*

CHARLOTTE

THIS BOOK BELONGS TO:

_____

Why Do You Want to Keep Bees?
What Do You Hope to Accomplish?

_____

_____

_____

_____

BEGINNING BEEKEEPING RECORD

Ordered Bees		
Ordered Basic Equipment		
Attended local bee club meeting		
Met another beginning beekeeper		
Scoped out hive locations		
Other		

Your Notes

_____

_____

_____

_____

_____

_____

_____

_____

_____

CHAPTER 1
Why Keep Honey Bees

HONEY BEES ARE IMPORTANT TO OUR FOOD SUPPLY

Honey bees are **nature's matchmakers,** moving pollen or male flower sperm, to plant ovaries inside flowers so plants make seed to reproduce. They are also **a keystone species,** responsible for the pollination of many important flowering plants.

- **90% of the 400,000 world plant species** depend on animal pollination.
- **75% of agricultural crops** rely on animal pollination.
- **One third of all agricultural crops** benefit from cross-pollination, developing higher fruit quality and quantity.

Bees, including honey bees and native bees, are **the largest of the pollinator group, responsible for 80% of all pollination.** They are followed by flies, wasps, hornets, birds and bats.

It will take a honey bee 1 to 500 flowers to gather a "full" load, depending on the flower, nectar and pollen production. A honey bee can visit and spread pollen from **75 to 3,000 flowers in one trip.** *One worker bee makes 5 drops of honey in her lifetime. It takes 556 bees visiting 2 million flowers to make one pound of honey. In photo, native pink phlox (Phlox paniculata.)*

- **Every third bite of healthy food we eat** is courtesy of pollinators.
- Insect pollination **enhances average crop yields between 18 and 71%** depending on the crop. Yield quality is also enhanced in most crops.
- Honey bee pollination **contributes at least $29 billion** annually to the US crop value.
- Honey bees **increase world crops by $235-$577 billion** a year.
- **Native bees contribute $9.1 billion a year** to world agricultural economy.
- Bees are **keystone or indicator species**, tracking an ecosystem's health. The decline in numbers of the Rusty Patched Bumble Bee and Monarch Butterfly in the Midwest reflect a decrease in habitat health.

HONEY BEES AS MAJOR POLLINATORS

- **Honey bees are generalists,** foraging on a wide variety of plants.
- **Nectar and pollen are their main food.** They also get vitamins, minerals and amino acids from microbial meat.
- Honey bees live all year.
- **Plumrose hair or branched body hairs** make them more efficient pollen collectors.
- **Flower constancy;** honey bees visit one flower species at a time.
- Honey bee colonies can be **easily moved and managed** to increase pollination.

HONEY BEES ARE NOT GOING EXTINCT

Honey bees were imported to North America in 1622. They are a managed species, similar to cattle. They are **not currently at risk of extinction** but they are facing major stressors as are native bees.

TODAY'S MAJOR BEE STRESSORS

- **Poor nutrition,** lack of foraging variety and healthy soils feeding the plants bees visit for nectar and pollen.
- **Pathogens** (chalkbrood, nosema, American foulbrood.)
- **Pests** such as *Varroa* mites (*varroa* destructor).

- **Overuse of pesticides,** including use when plants are blooming and attracting pollinators such as honey bees.

- **Poor management;** not following best management practices.

To address the impacts of these stressors, the US in 2016 published the science-based **Pollinator Research Action Plan** with these three goals:

1. **Reduce annual honey bee losses** to less than 15% over the next 10 years;

2. **Increase monarch populations** to at least 225 million at Mexican wintering grounds by 2020; and

3. **Restore and enhance 7 million acres of pollinator habitat** across the country through public-private landholder relationships.

There are a number of state and federal programs that offer incentives to encourage more pollinator habitat. In Missouri, for example, the **Missourians for Monarchs Collaborative** represents more than 100 state and federal agencies focused on planting 385,000 pollinator habitat acres over 20 years, or 19,000 acres per year. Missouri sits in the middle of the monarch butterfly migratory highway, making it one of the key states to feed the pollinators as they move up and down the continent.

By the end of 2019, the **partners had reported surpassing their** 385,000 acres goal.

*Pollen-covered **Missouri native carpenter bee** in my Missouri hillside garden. Some solitary native bees use sonication, vibrating flight muscles without moving its wings, to shake pollen out of flowers.*

NATIVE BEES

There are **20,000 bee species worldwide.** North America is home to 4,000 native bee species with **Missouri home to 450 unique bee species.**

- **Current native wild bee populations are on the decline** due to habitat loss, lack of forage and pesticide exposure.

- Some **native bees have an interdependent relationship with specific plants.** In 2017, the Rusty Patched Bumble Bee *(Bombus affinis)* was listed on International Union for Conservation of Nature's Red List of Threatened Species. The listing means they are facing imminent extinction.

- **Native bees are more efficient pollinators** than honey bees but are available for much shorter periods of time.

NATIVE BEE CARE TIPS

Get a start on keeping bees by **encouraging native bees:**

- Hang native bee houses in a **protected garage or shed over winter.**

- **Move houses out when blossoms are starting to swell** and the chance of frost is low, usually when temperatures consistently exceed 50F. Place houses **within 100 feet or less** of fruit trees.

- Bees will emerge 1-14 days after warming up.

- **Place your native bee house** in your garden **against a flat surface protected from high winds.** Face the house south or southwest where it will get the most sun.

- Mason bee cocoons can also be released when temperatures are consistently above 50F in your area.

- Some species need a **ready source of mud** to seal their nesting areas.

- **Most native bees are specialists,** depending on certain plants and plant families for their food. Their hatching schedule coincides with their host flowers blooming schedule.

- **Leave open ground** for nesting and mud access.

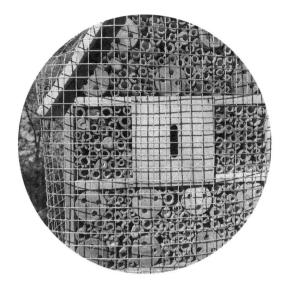

*Cover your native bee houses **with chicken wire** to protect slumbering bees from becoming easy bird snacks. **Replace used tubes annually.***

COMMON MIDWEST NATIVE BEES

Bumblebees *(Bombus spp)* There are 10 known Missouri species. Bumbles are robust, hairy bees that make a middle C sound as they vibrate plants to release pollen, such as tomatoes. They have long tongues (proboscis) allowing them to reach deep into narrow tubular flowers. Black body covered with black, yellow, brownish or orange hair bands; pollen baskets on hind legs. Nest underground and live in social colonies. They also fly and orient better in greenhouses and in colder climates than honey bees. **They pollinate tomatoes, peppers, eggplants and berries.**

Carpenter Bees *(Xylocopa virginica, Ceratina spp.)* One native Missouri species. Stingless males hover, patrolling a territory for females, chasing away other bees and even humans. They are bees that drill holes in wood to nest. Black body with light or dark hairs, similar body shape to bumble bee but abdomen shiny with sparse hairs. **Live in both solitary and communal nests burrowed in wood.**

Small Carpenter Bees *(Ceratina)* have shiny dark metallic blue-green body and sparsely haired, cylindrical abdomens and pollen carrying hairs on hind legs. **They nest in dead twigs and stems.**

Digger/Mining Bees *(Andrena spp.)* Solitary or communal ground nesters abundant in spring; they are one of the first bees to emerge each season. Black or dull metallic body often with brown or reddish hairs; pollen carrying hairs on upper parts of hind legs and side of thorax appearing to carry pollen in its "armpit."

Leafcutter and Mason Bees *(Megachile spp. & Osmia spp.)* Also solitary bees that live in man-made holes such as beetle holes, nesting blocks, stems and soil. Head as broad as thorax; large mandibles; black body most with pale bands on abdomen (metallic green or blue for Osmia); pollen carrying hairs under abdomen. Females cut circular pieces from leaves to line their nests. The Orchard Mason bees (Osmia) collect mud, resin, or leaf hairs for nesting. They do not provide honey or other products.

Alfalfa Leafcutter Bees *(Megachile rotundata)* are intensively managed for the pollination of alfalfa, canola and seed clover. Alfalfa is a primary feed source for cattle; **Alfalfa Leafcutter bees can triple seed production.**

Blue Orchard Mason Bee *(Osmia lignaria)* has become established as an alternative orchard pollinator in North America. Together with honey bees, **these native bee species are used commercially to pollinate fruit and nut orchards.** Their nests are covered in mud. They rarely sting. Current research is focusing on how to keep them in one area; they currently are not site loyal.

Long Horned Bees *(Melissodes, Svastra app)* Solitary to communal ground nesters. Stout robust hairy body often with pale hair bands on abdomen; dense pollen carrying hairs on hind legs. Males have antennae as long as body. **Especially attracted to asters, sunflowers, daisies and relative species.**

Squash Bees (*Peponapis pruinose)* Solitary ground nesters often in or near pumpkins and squash fields. Brownish, honey-bee sized with light spot on face. Males have long antennae. Coarse dense pollen collecting hair on hind legs. **They only collect pollen from squash/pumpkins.**

Sweat Bees *(Agapostemon, Holictus, Lasioglossum ssp.)* Iridescent green, dull metallic blue, copper or green metallic color with pollen-carrying hairs on hind legs. Solitary to highly social ground nesters. **Some are attracted to salt in human sweat.**

Yellow Jackets *(Hymenoptera Vespula or Dolichovespula)* Not a bee but often mistaken for one. Yellow jackets are wasps that live in ground nests. They can both continuously sting and bite when provoked, as when you **mow over their nest with your lawn mower.**

AFRICANIZED BEES *(Apis mellifera hybrid)*

The **Africanized bee,** also known as the **Africanized honey bee** and colloquially as the **"killer bee",** is a western honey bee hybrid. It was originally bred by crossing an East African lowland honey bee *(A.m. scutellata)* with various European honey bees including the Italian honey bee *(A.m. iberiensis)*

The Africanized honey bee was **first introduced to Brazil in 1956** in an effort to increase honey production. In 1957, 26 swarms escaped quarantine. Since then, the hybrid has spread throughout South America and **arrived in North America in 1985.**

Africanized bees are excellent honey producers, resistant to *Varroa* mites and well suited to tropical climates. They are highly defensive and aggressive, and readily swarm.

They are also the predominant bees used in Central and South America beekeeping. **Currently cold winter weather keeps Africanized bees to the southern US states.**

All European honey bee species can **cross fertilize with Africanized bees.** There are 29 recognized *Apis mellifera* subspecies based largely on geographic variations.

MIGRATORY BEEKEEPING

We enjoy a varied diet with fruits, vegetables, nuts and seeds in large measure to migratory beekeepers. The practice of moving hives originated for a different purpose - better honey production.

Today approximately **1,600 US migratory beekeepers** move 2.5 million honey bee colonies for nearly 90 crops grown on 3.5 million acres to provide farmers with crop pollination services.

- Honey bees significantly increase food production **by pollinating plants and increasing their quality and yield.**
- To maximize yield, colonies are placed in monocultural fields where their **sole source of nectar and pollen** is one crop.
- The best time to move honey bee colonies into a targeted field is when plants are **20-40% into their blooming cycle.**
- Bees forage best **within about 100 yards** of the hive.
- **There is an average of 5 days** when blooming plants are poised for pollination. Bees managed for pollination rental is similar to managing bees for honey production.

Approximately 60% of all US honey bee hives move west in February to help pollinate 2.5 trillion flowers in California's nearly 1 million acres of almond trees over a two-week period. 80% of world's almond supply comes from California, USA.

- **Bees are supplement-fed** to produce large, expanding colonies at bloom time.

- **Feeding sugar syrup** simulates a nectar flow and produces a higher proportion of pollen collection among foragers.
- **Beekeepers continue to manage** bees while on pollination sites.
- **Colonies need to be established** to be effective pollinators. Hiving package bees two to three weeks before pollination rental will not provide efficient pollinator services.

BEEKEEPING ON WHEELS

Migratory beekeepers tend to spend **six months out of the year** on the move with their colonies.

- Colonies in general are **moved at night** to maintain foraging population.
- Colonies are **moved on pallets** with heavy equipment that can easily load and move them.
- In warmer weather, **a moving screen** may replace top of hive covers to keep bees cool.
- Some states **require colony inspections** before hives enter the state.
- **Theft of migratory colonies** has become an increasing issue for migratory beekeepers.

*Migratory beekeepers move bees on the back of trucks **covered in netting**.*

SAMPLE US MIGRATORY BEEKEEPING POLLINATION SCHEDULE

Migratory beekeepers monitor **weather conditions, estimated bloom times** and the **highest economic return** on their investment, among other factors, to determine which crops they plan to pollinate.

The following is a **list of major crops** and, in general, when they get pollinated to increase commercial yield:

LATE WINTER AND SPRING	SUMMER*
Almonds: California *Apples, cherries and plums:* Washington State	*Alfalfa, sunflowers, clover:* North and South Dakota *Watermelons, Cantaloupes, Cucumbers, Squash:* Texas *Clementines and Tangerines:* Florida *Cranberries:* Wisconsin *Blueberries:* Michigan and Maine *The **Missouri Bootheel** sees hives brought in for watermelons. The central area of the state gets hives to supplement apple pollination.

Most migratory colonies spend winter in **California, Texas, Florida** and, at times, stored in **Idaho potato cellars.**

The estimated value of honey bee pollination services **now surpasses** the value of honey produced.

STATIONARY HONEY BEES AND MIGRATORY BEEKEEPING

Stationary honey bees tend to be **healthier and more productive** because they have:

- **Less stress** from travel.
- **Less exposure** to pests and diseases.
- **Healthier foraging in a variety of pollen sources.** Good nutrition requires having **at least six different kinds of pollen** available during brood rearing.

To **easily provide** a variety of pollen sources:

- Mix legumes, such as White-Dutch Clover and Hairy Vetch, in any ground covers for under trees and orchards.
- Drainages and fence lines can be left to revert to a wild state. Large 10-20 foot strips can be maintained to encourage pollinators.
- Crop rotation and leaving areas fallow yearly can encourage diverse annuals and be mowed after frost or in early spring.

(VERY) SHORT HISTORY OF BEEKEEPING

Humans have been beekeepers **for many centuries.** The latest scientific findings place the use of honey products at least 9,000 years ago.

One of the most popular references to honey is associated with the discovery in 1922 of King Tutankhamun's tomb in Egypt. **Honey stored in vessels buried 3,000 years ago were reportedly still edible.**

The native **North American honey bee** became extinct 17 million years ago. It was recently discovered in a Colorado archaeological dig and identified by its unique wing structure.

European settlers brought the black German bee *Apis mellifera* to North American **in 1622.** Native American Indians called the honey bee **the "white man's fly"** because honey bee swarms often preceded European settlers moving west.

Honey bees were not only an **inexpensive source of sweetener.** They were also a source of **wax for candles,** the only light they had besides fire; handy home improvement – **beeswax was used like a caulk to weather strip their homes** - and to **seal homemade medicinal potions** made from herbs they grew. Honey was also the **source of mead**, a fermented alcoholic drink, second only to beer as their drink of choice.

MISSOURI'S (QUIRKY) HONEY WAR

Missouri has the distinction of hosting the quirky bloodless **1839 Honey War.** It was a politically swaggering territorial dispute between Iowa and Missouri over their shared boundary line and who went where to **collect taxes on bee trees.**

The dispute started in 1837 when a Missourian cut three "bee trees" in a border area both states claimed. In those days, bee hunters **"lined" bees,** following the bees from water or nectar-collecting areas back to their hives. (Does the expression make a "bee line" sound familiar?)

The bee trees were valuable both for the honey - **$.37 cents a gallon** - and even more for the valuable beeswax. Beeswax was prized for candles and sealing bottles, medicinal as well as alcoholic. **Not to mention the taxes.**

Iowa claimed that the bee trees were in their territory. They "tried" the Missouri bee tree "thief" in absentia. He was **fined $1.50**, which did not go well on the feisty Missouri side.

There were several more escalating exchanges between the Missouri and Iowa governors. A bedraggled Missouri sheriff was repeatedly ordered, and failed, to collect the bee tree taxes from what was by then called the **"seat of excitement."**

In 1839, both states rallied their rag tag militia and were ready for a fight. **Missouri claimed an edge with a sausage stuffer.**

Early December 1839, Missouri troops were rallied in the cold with few tents and blankets but plenty of booze. They split a haunch of venison, labeling one side for each of the Missouri and Iowa governors. **After shooting them full of holes,** they held a mock funeral. Then both sides made a rowdy retreat. The "war' was officially over.

The US Supreme Court ultimately settled **in Iowa's favor.**

In 1850, **the two states compromised** on a state line close to the middle of the four possible boundaries. Markers were set every 10 miles. **Only one marker** remains today noting the "seat of excitement." The three bee trees **were cut down.**

No word on what happened to the sausage stuffer.

WHAT IS A BEE SKEP?

*The "skep" is a **popular symbol of beekeeping.** It has been adopted by several US states to represent industry and hard work.*

The **symbol of beekeeping is a tool that is no longer used by most US beekeepers.** The bee skep is a woven basket that was used to keep bees. To harvest the honey, the bees had to be destroyed.

Today **states that regulate beekeeping require bees to be kept in hives with removable frames.**

In spite of the changes in beekeeping, the bee skep remains a popular symbol of the practice of keeping bees.

ANCIENT VOCATION NOW HAS A MODERN TWIST

Reverend Lorenzo Lorraine Langstroth is considered the father of US beekeeping. In 1852, he introduced the age of more **standardized and less destructive** beekeeping with the invention of hives with removable frames. Up until the development of the Langstroth hive, beekeepers would keep bees in a wide range of equipment from trees to baskets. Bees in trees didn't allow for brood disease inspections.

Langstroth also revolutionized beekeeping with **"bee space," the 3/8th inch of space,** the width of **two honey bees**, that makes working with bees easier.

- In the summer of 1851, Langstroth discovered that by leaving an even, approximately bee-sized space between the top of the frames and the hive top, he was able to easily remove the coverboard. When there was more space, bees would cement the frames with propolis, a bee glue made from tree sap; propolis is now recognized as having antibacterial properties in a hive.

- He later used this discovery to make the **frames themselves easily removable.** If a small space was left (less than 1/4 inch or 6.4 mm) the bees filled it with propolis; on the other hand, when a larger space was left (more than 3/8 inch or 9.5 mm) the bees filled it with comb. **Today observing bee space is an important element in successful beekeeping.**

WHY SO MANY DIFFERENT ANSWERS?

And now, a short break to address one of the proverbial comments, complaints and, dare I say, frustrations from beginning beekeepers. The correct answer to most, if not all beekeeping questions is:

IT DEPENDS

That's because bees are **living creatures**. It is **up to us as beekeepers** to keep up with them, not direct them on what to do. It is a major shift in the lives of people who think they are in charge, and a shift some people don't easily make. **To be a successful beekeeper, one has to listen, and for the most part take their cues from the bees.**

Your goal as a successful beekeeper is to **stay two steps ahead and plan six months ahead. Yes, it's the fine art of juggling and requires the beekeeper to stay flexible.**

There are several other reasons why you may get different answers:

1. **Objectives.** Beekeepers keep bees for different reasons. Beekeeping **techniques will vary** depending on the beekeeper's objectives:

    A. Pollination

    B. Honey

    C. To raise more bees

    D. To observe one of nature's amazing creatures

2. **Method.** Beekeepers are landlords providing a home for living creatures in a variety of different equipment. **Each has their own unique challenges and advantages.**

   Some—well, let's be honest, a good number of beekeepers—keep bees with homemade contraptions added. To understand how those homemade additions work, **you have to first understand** why the beekeeper made them in the first place.

3. **Environmental impacts.** Bees are affected by their environment including **pesticide exposure, foraging food quality, pests, diseases, and pathogens.**

   Some beekeepers don't focus or even discuss "other" beekeeping aspects such as the quality of plants bees visit for food. Or what they plant for their bees, if anything. **The quality and variety of plant foods significantly impact bee health.**

4. **Level of experience.** Beekeepers will share what worked for them. That can **vary from beekeeper to beekeeper** depending on how long they have been beekeeping and how much experience they have working apiaries.

   Beekeepers who have been keeping bees for many years **may not know the latest techniques** and **environmental impacts** now affecting bees.

   On the other hand, some successful experienced beekeepers can have a lot to offer. **The challenge is sorting through what is still appropriate today.**

5. **"Location, Location, Location."** Beekeeping can vary from place to place, even those located nearby. Something that **works in one area may not be appropriate for another area.**

6. **Lack of training.** Some beekeepers like to talk based solely on personal experience and **haven't pursued formal training** on how to keep bees. There are some basic scientifically based, state of the art beekeeping principles that all beekeepers should know to effectively manage bees.

   Look for beekeeping classes that are associated with **professionally run and scientifically based** beekeeping programs.

7. **Confusing and wrong terminology.** As a beginning beekeeper, **learning beekeeping terms** is critical to your being able to effectively and accurately communicate.

   Some confusion comes from beginning beekeepers not being able to effectively explain what they saw. They may also use terminology incorrectly. Focus on learning **what beekeeping equipment is called** and what **names describe its various uses.**

   Beekeeping equipment may have different terms according to their use.

8. **Active listening.** If you are confused or don't understand, keep **asking clarifying questions.** Then listen. **Take time** to relate the information to something you already know. Most beekeeping answers have **ranges and probabilities,** not certainties.

9. **Keep an open mind.** Some beekeepers ask questions wanting to confirm a pre-conceived idea.

   Keep an open mind. **You may be surprised by the answer and learn something.**

10. **Do your own research. Read.** Successful beekeeping includes juggling information and updating what you just learned.

    There will be some facts that you won't be able to pin down and that's ok, **beekeeping today is fluid** as new information is being discovered.

11. *Varroa* **mites do exist, even if you can't see them.** Check out my April 2018 video of *Varroa* **mites** in brood comb: **bit.ly/***varroa***-mites.**

    As a beekeeper, you will be working with two arthropods—honey bees and *Varroa* **mites.** You want to keep one successfully inside hives and keep the other one in smallest numbers possible. **Understand the life cycle of both honey bees, the** *Varroa* ***destructor*** mite and how they impact each other. *Varroa* mites are now throughout North American bee colonies.

    New recommendations, approaches and products have been **evolving annually;** stay on top of **current research and scientifically based recommendations.**

12. **Treatment free.** We would all like to go back to the days when only wax moths were the beekeeper's main challenge. That's not where we find ourselves.

    Currently **40% of managed hives die every winter,** which is not a sustainable number.

    As scientists breed new traits and find new methods to deal with honey bee stressors, it is **our responsibility to follow best management practices** to keep our bees healthy.

    Not feeding, not treating, not checking – makes us "bee havers," not "bee keepers."

13. **No easy answers.** Honey bees are living creatures. They **also change and adjust to their circumstances** and don't necessarily explain themselves. Or, as we like to say, bees don't read the beekeeping books.

I know as beginning beekeepers you would like to have **absolutes. There are few.** Successful beekeeping is contingent on beekeepers observing, tracking and learning from the bees.

Often times the new beekeeper's challenge is to watch and observe, staying out of the way of the bees, and learn from them. **Bees know what they are doing.**

We are lucky as a beekeeping community to have **dedicated scientists** focusing on current issues and willing to share their findings. **Keep up with the new science.**

14. **Things change. And fast!** When starting to keep bees, one of the more often-asked questions is **how often to inspect a hive.**

(You see it coming, don't you?)

Well, it depends. How developed is the colony; what time of year is it, what do you observe your honey bees doing.

You could be inspecting them – that's going through the frames – every few days or leaving them to settle in for a week or two. Or both, **depending on what the bees are doing.**

ARE THERE OTHER OPTIONS?

Yes but some are challenging. One of the more frequent suggestions is to "find a mentor."

Experienced beekeepers may answer questions but usually don't have time to help beginners. Mentors also will not do the actual beekeeping; good ones will describe and perhaps demonstrate to and for you, and then give you feedback as you do what they described. But you first need to know the terminology, have the necessary equipment and be ready when they are.

It may be easier to find a **"bee buddy,"** someone who is starting this adventure when you are. Then you can share what you are learning, visit each other's apiaries and borrow equipment as needed.

It IS scary. I can still remember the first time I opened up a hive lid all by myself. Take the initiative and, when conditions are right, get to it. In the end, the **bees are the best teachers.**

WHY DO YOU WANT TO KEEP HONEY BEES?
(Check all that apply)

REASON	SPECIFICS	MAJOR HELP	POSSIBLE CHALLENGES
☐ Pollination	What trees, shrubs, flowers are blooming April-Oct. within 2 miles of your hive location(s)?		
☐ Pesticides	Any pesticide use within 5 miles. If so, what kind?		
☐ Pets	Do you have time to care for bees as you would pets? Are there others who may share your interest?		
☐ Honey	• For allergies • For consumption • To sell • To make products	*(List products)*	*(List challenges)*
☐ "Save Bees"	Honey bees are not in danger; native bees are the ones currently at risk. Keeping honey bees is not directly connected to conserving native bees.		
☐ Bee Business	• To sell honey • To sell bees • To sell hive products		
☐ Education	To learn about the fascinating world of apiculture (beekeeping)		

CHECK YOUR APIARY LAWS

One of the first steps considering keeping bees is to **know your local, county and state apiary laws.**

You will find your local laws at your local city government office:

- **Check with** the planning and zoning department for specifics; ask the city clerk for copies of your local ordinances.
- **County government may also have laws** that impact beekeeping. Your county clerk should have details. Sometimes county health departments may also be familiar with provisions. Double check any updates in laws through your state Legislature's main library.
- **Do not depend only on an internet search** for the latest information; go to the original source for accurate information.

If you live in a managed community, **there may be restrictions and other covenants** regulating how many colonies are allowed on your property. Check your contract for any restrictions.

Another source of local beekeeping laws is your **local bee club.** Attending local bee club meetings is an excellent way to find out not only what laws exist that impact bees but how established beekeepers manage the provisions.

BEE HIVES AND EQUIPMENT ASSESSED AS PERSONAL PROPERTY

In states with personal property taxes, **bee hives may be assessed as property** and annually taxed.

Beekeeping equipment, such as an extractor, may also be required to be listed as personal property.

BEST MANAGEMENT PRACTICES

The best source of a good beekeeping foundation is to **look for scientifically-based, recommended best management practices.** Many beekeeping programs, and beekeeping associations, have those for their areas and states. This book and the beginning beekeeping class have been reviewed by the Great Plains Master Beekeeping Program out of the University of Nebraska at Lincoln.

You will find recommended best management practices on **beekeeping group and association websites.**

The beekeeping pledge in this book is based on Missouri's recommended best management practices.

We hear a lot about Reverend L.L. Langstroth being the father of modern US beekeeping. But do you know who made beekeeping safer by inventing the beekeeper's best friend? **Moses Quinby** *(April 15 or 16, 1810 – May 26, 1875)* was a New York beekeeper. He is remembered as the "Father" of practical Beekeeping and the "Father" of US commercial beekeeping. He is best known as the inventor of the bee smoker with bellows that helps beekeepers more safely get into hives. *(Courtesy Wikipedia)*

*Over the years, smokers have evolved from a **variety of shapes.***

AS YOU CONSIDER KEEPING HONEY BEES...

GOOD THINGS TO DO	NOTES
Checked local, regional and state laws concerning beekeeping in your area?	
Inventoried your property for the trees, shrubs and plants growing on and around your property and the surrounding 2 miles, and when they bloom?	
Picked up beekeeping books and equipment catalogs to get to know terminology?	
Checked out current beekeeping books from your local public library to read and study? Focus on beginning beekeeping books to get the basic concepts down.	
Shadowed another practicing beekeeper?	
Been inside a beehive?	
Attended local beekeeping club meetings?	
Watched videos appropriate to beekeeping conditions where you live? Get recommended video list from your local bee club; not all videos apply to your area.	
Attended a beginning beekeeping class?	
Identified a dry storage area at your home for beekeeping equipment?	

Kept bees before? When? Beekeeping practices changed significantly after the impact of *Varroa* mites.	
Evaluated your physical ability to handle hives and beekeeping? It takes strength to lift hives and supers.	
Discussed with your family your interest in adding honey bees to your garden? Is there someone else who would like to learn and help?	
Assessed how your close neighbors feel about you adding hives to the neighborhood?	
Have you tasted local honey? Had comb honey on toast?	
Do you know the difference between *a bee sting and a wasp sting?*	
Can you identify a honey bee from a yellow jacket wasp?	
Have you purchased local honey from a beekeeper at your local farmer's market and compared it to imported store-purchased honey?	
Other:	

Your Notes

_____

_____

_____

_____

_____

_____

_____

_____

_____

Your Notes

_____

_____

_____

_____

_____

_____

_____

_____

_____

CHAPTER 2

Feeding Bees Naturally

BEES NEED A VARIETY OF FOOD SOURCES

Your bees need to eat. They need real flower nectar, pollen and the associated vitamins, minerals and amino acids plants produce.

Bees do not forage for pollen and nectar on the same trip. Guided by different floral pheromones or scents, colors and markings, honey bees collect **flower nectar for flight fuel and energy,** and **flower pollen** nurse bees turn into baby food.

Honey bees collect **flower nectar for flight fuel and energy,** and **flower pollen for baby food.** Plants, in turn, attract pollinators with sweet nectar, a reward for matchmaking services.

Pollinators move pollen from one plant to ovaries deep inside another plant **to produce seeds.** We depend on that process to add variety to our food; **one out of every three bites of healthy food we eat are courtesy of bee pollination.**

A honey bee visits Iris in my apiary. Aphids secrete a sticky sugar-ish liquid as they feed on plant sap called honeydew. **Honeydew honey** *is generally dark, strongly flavored, less acidic and less sweet than floral honey.*

SAMPLE BEE POLLINATED CROPS FOR SEED AND FRUIT PRODUCTION

Asparagus	Celery	Mustard
Broccoli	Collards	Onions
Brussel sprouts	Garlic	Parsley
Cabbage	Kohlrabi	Radish
Carrots	Leeks	Rutabaga
Cauliflower	Lima Beans	Turnips

SAMPLE BEE POLLINATED NATIVE FRUITS

Blackberries	Dewberries	Passion Fruit
Blueberries	Gooseberries	Paw-Paws
Cranberries	Grapes	Persimmon

INTRODUCED FRUITS POLLINATED BY BEES

Almonds	Melons	Peppers
Apples	Peaches	Tomatoes
Cucumbers	Pears	Watermelons

Yellow (and White) Sweet Clover (Melilotus officinalis) is a legume native to Eurasia and introduced to North America. It survives one winter. If conditions are right, it is a good source of nectar and pollen but bees can't live on sweet clover, or any one crop, alone. The more variety of pollen and nectar sources the better!

TIPS ON PLANTING FOR HONEY BEES

- What kind of soil do you have? **Get a soil test** from your local *extension office to find out what will grow best in the soil you have. The test will also provide suggestions on how to improve your soil.*

- **Plant away from hives.** Honey bees ignore a radius of approximately 50 feet from the hive; that area may be contaminated by their cleansing flights.

- **Provide plants in Spring**, when colonies are building up, **and Fall**, when colonies are getting ready for winter. Flowering plants are usually available through summer.

- Research shows good bee nutrition requires **at least six different kinds** of pollen available during brood rearing.

- Also provide hardy plants during the hottest months. Missouri's August dearth, for example, has temperatures over 86°F for weeks, which prompts plants to switch to survival mode and shut down nectar and pollen production. **Plant perennials that tolerate the higher temperatures.**

- In general, **honey bees forage within a 2 mile radius** of their home. The closer the food supply is to their hives, the more productive they will be. They may fly up to 5 miles if food sources are scarce.

- **Plant species in large swaths.** Honey bees collect nectar and pollen from all of one flower source before moving on to a next one. That's why flower beds with at least **3 to 5 plants of the same species** provide honey bees a good foraging bed.

- **Bees see flowers differently than we do.** Flowers use scent, patterns, nectar, electrical charges and ultraviolet colors to **attract** bees. In some cases, their markings and colors are ones we humans can't see. **In general, bees like blue, yellow and white flowers.** They don't "see" the color red.

- Bees need at least six different flower sources to feed brood.

*When selecting plants for bees, **choose flowers with single flower petals**, such as chicory, so bees can easily access pollen and nectar. Hybrid and flowers with double petals are pretty but their flower nectaries, where flowers produce nectar, are not accessible to bees.*

MAJOR HONEY BEE PLANT FAMILIES

Honey bees get nectar and pollen from **six major plant families**, which have a variety of trees, shrubs and flowers in each family.

Asters (*daisy-shaped flowers*)	**Mint** (*herbs*)
Figwort (*butterfly bush*)	**Mustard** (*flowering broccoli*)
Legumes (*buckwheat*)	**Rosaceae** (*berries*)

MIDWEST ANNUAL BEE PLANT EXAMPLES

(Annuals grow from seed for one growing season)

COMMON NAME	SCIENTIFIC NAME
Sweet Alyssum	*Labularia maritima*
Bachelor's Button/Cornflower	*Centaurea cyanus*
Cosmos	*Cosmos bipinnatus*
Marigold (*single blooming*)*	*Tagetes spp.*
Sunflowers (*single blooming*)*	*Helianthus annuus*
Zinnias	*Zinnia spp.*

The single petal shape allows pollinators to easy reach nectar and pollen. Doubles and hybrids can impede access.

*Annual zinnias are easy to grow in most soils. They are also **popular sources of summer bee food.** If you are just starting a garden, **plant zinnias.***

MIDWEST PERENNIAL NATIVE PLANT EXAMPLES
(Once planted, perennials grow back yearly on their own)

COMMON NAME	SCIENTIFIC NAME
Asters, New England	*S. novae-angliae*
Beardtongue	*P. digitalis*
Bee Balm	*M. punctata*
Cardinal Flower, Red	*L. cardinalis*
Goldenrod, Showy	*S. speciosa*
Indigo, Blue	*A. australis*
Joe Pye Weed	*E. dubium*
Phlox	*P. paniculata*

MIDWEST TREE EXAMPLES FOR BEE FOOD

COMMON NAME	SCIENTIFIC NAME
Dogwood, Flowering	*Cornus florida*
Elderberry	*Sambucus canadensis*
Pawpaw	*Asimina triloba*
Serviceberry	*Amelanchier arborea*
Witch-hazel	*Hamamelis vernalis*

*Invasive **bush honeysuckle, often mistaken for honeysuckle,** produces red berries in fall encouraging birds to distribute seeds. **Bush honeysuckle** does not provide bees food and is deadly to plants growing under it. Corn, barley and wheat self pollinate and don't provide bees food, either.*

INVASIVE PLANTS

Some beekeepers welcome invasive plants because **they provide honey bees with a ready source of nectar and pollen.** However, invasive plants **destroy an area's biodiversity,** working against the health of the interdependent ecosystems. Some invasive species, such as bush honeysuckle, do not have any value to bees and kill everything that grows under and near them.

Research has shown **there are 22 times fewer insects in a hedgerow made up of invasive and nonnative species** than a hedgerow made up of native plants.

Some states, such as Missouri, have **collaborative invasive exotic plant species task forces** focused on removing the most damaging invasive plants. The good news is that once invasive plants are removed, **most native plants are resilient.** In most cases, native plants will grow back and easily get re-established.

TOP TEN MIDWEST INVASIVE PLANTS

1. **Burning Bush** (*Euonymus alatus*)
2. **Bush honeysuckle** (*Lonicera maackii*)
3. **Autumn Olive** (*Elaeagnus umbellate*)
4. **Japanese honeysuckle** (*Lonicera japonica*)
5. **Oriental bittersweet** (*Celastrus orbiculatus*)
6. **Wintercreeper** (*Euonymus fortune*)
7. **Callery/Bradford pear** (*Pyrus calleryana*)
8. **Garlic mustard** (*Alliaria petiolate*)
9. **Sericea lespedeza** (*Lespedeza cuneate*)
10. **Johnson grass** (*Sorghum hapalense*)

WHY PLANT NATIVE PLANTS

If you are a beginning gardener, **natives will grow better and get established faster and more easily** for you. Remember to water until they become established; **just because they are native** doesn't mean **they don't need moisture.**

If you are an experienced gardener, you understand the interdependent connection between natives, local soil and topography and the creatures that make those plants, and areas, their home.

- Concentrate on planting plants that will feed your local native insects and pollinators.
- Native plants get easily established because they are acclimated to your soil, weather and climate.

There are a number of **private, state, and federal programs ready to lend advice, assistance and even free and/or discounted seeds.** Check with your state conservation agencies and agriculture-related federal and non-governmental groups.

OTHER TIPS ON PLANTING FOR BEES

When planting, remember your bees will decide what plants they will visit, and they may not be in your yard.

- **Keep your soil healthy.** Compost; mulch; add manure. Wait six months for manure to integrate into soil.
- Don't know where to start? Have at least **25 types of different trees, shrubs and perennials continuously blooming** at once through the growing season. For a starter. It takes **2 million flowers to make one pound of honey** so yes, that's a lot of flowers. In other words, there's no such thing as too many flowers.
- **Plant microclover** (*Trifolium repens L. var. Pirouette*) in lieu of turf grass. It has smaller leaves and a lower growth habit. More flowers are retained when mowed, providing pollinators more food sources.
- **Companion plant** to reduce bug damage without using pesticides.
- Check Pollinator.org for **US region specific planting guides** for farmers, land managers and gardeners. You will find the planting guide for your region and for Canadian provinces by entering your zip code. **Starting on page 16 of the planting guides,** you will find lists of plant names that will support pollinators including bees. Print those lists and bring them to your local native plant, garden center and nursery.

HOW TO REMOVE UNWANTED PLANTS

- Pull them
- Pour boiling water onto them
- Plant stronger, native plants
- Smother with cardboard/newspapers
- Douse with vinegar
- Eat them; most unwanted plants are herbs!

DON'T USE PESTICIDES

Not all pesticides are equally dangerous to bees but they are a leading cause of bee decline.

Read labels before buying and applying.

- **Follow directions!**
- For immediate bug relief, mix dish washing liquid drops in a water-full spray bottle; add hot sauce to amp it up. Re-spray on plants with bugs you don't want after a rain. **Don't use on bees unless you want to kill them.**

Studies show homeowners are the leading misusers of pesticides. In particular:

- Product labels **are not read** and/or **correctly applied.**
- **More product is not** necessarily **more effective**.
- Products are **applied when plants are in bloom,** which is when pollinators are exposed to the products.

Don't mix herbicides, insecticides and pesticides. Recent studies show some large bee deaths were as the result of applicators mixing these products. One of the most common symptoms of bee pesticide poisoning is large numbers of dead and/or dying bees at ground level or at hive entrances.

PLANTING WILDFLOWERS AND BEE PASTURES

Planting wildflowers and bee pastures **are designed to provide quality food for native bees,** which are also excellent crop pollinators. Native bees live for shorter periods of time than honey bees. They are more efficient pollinators for the short time frame they are working flowers.

In some areas, **wildflowers are planted along public access road shoulders, fence rows and as buffer strips around field crops,** providing both native and honey bees more foraging variety and extending the blooming season.

There are **three types of wildflower plantings:**

1. **One-year bee pastures** are focused on providing annual clovers, wildflowers and ornamental shrubs that collectively bloom for most of one forage season. They have to be reseeded every year and require little extra maintenance. *To provide full-season bloom coverage, they require large planted acreage.*

2. **Multi-year bee pastures** provide perennial blooming flowers, woody vines and bushes. This planting requires advanced planning to provide blooms all through

the growing season but can easily be developed in otherwise unproductive areas such as fence rows. *These areas require more plant management to maintain from trimming shrubs to dividing crowded plants.*

3. **Permanent bee pastures** have trees, bushes and woody plants that live more than 30 years. Plant selection is critical to ensure a continuously bloom through the growing season. Initially these permanent areas are expensive to set up. Over the long run, however, they don't require plowing, weeding or fertilizing, making them good economical investments. *Permanent bee pastures work best for fruit and vegetable growers who want permanent, large wild bee populations.*

4. **Land management agencies offer assistance** from free and discounted seeds to helping develop wildflower planting plans. Check with your state conservation agencies for what help they can provide.

PLANTING FOR NATIVE BEES AND OTHER POLLINATORS

Establish perennial native wildflower gardens with:

1. A **minimum of 25 different plant species** providing flowers that bloom at different times through the growing season.

   - **Pick a mix of species** that offer a variety of color and blooms **April to October.** According to research, native plants such as grayhead coneflower, golden Alexanders and leadplant are necessary for promoting bee diversity.
   - Plant and manage for **native flowering shrubs,** such as false wild indigo and wild plum.

2. **Build bee nest structures** for a number of native bee species.

3. **Use native wildflower and shrub plantings** to connect habitats, such as hedgerows, riparian areas, and brushy roadsides. Plant unproductive areas on farms, such as center pivot irrigation corners and field borders sapped by trees in fence lines.

4. Edge feathering, the practice of chopping and dropping trees along hedgerows, can be used to **increase the amount of downed dead wood and stumps for mason bees.**

5. **Maintain undisturbed areas** of bare ground for native miner bees and sweat bees. They make their nests in the ground and need an area free of plant litter to build their nest tunnels.

6. Bumblebee nesting sites are typically found in native warm-season bunch grasses, such as little bluestem or prairie dropseed. **Leave weedy patches so bumbles have nesting areas.**

7. Prescribed burning is useful in maintaining pollinator plantings and controlling some invasive species. Research shows prescribed burning increases bee ground nesting because it reduces plant litter. **To protect bees, burning should be conducted between October and February.** No more than one-third of a field should be treated at any one time.

8. **Leave patches of lawn, field, or edge habitat untouched throughout the entire year.** If mowing is necessary, do so with your blade raised to the highest height possible to avoid damaging nests or overwintering queen bumblebees. Some of the smallest bee species will overwinter in the stems of wildflowers and weeds.

9. Don't forget to **plant and protect pollinators' host plants**, such as milkweeds for monarchs and spicebush for spicebush swallowtail butterflies.

10. **In Fall, let leaves fall and get composted in growing areas.** Leaves add organic matter and improve soil and provide cover for beneficial garden residents such as ladybugs.

11. **Provide a safe water source** within a quarter mile of your hives throughout the growing season. When using bird baths, add rocks and twigs to give pollinators safe landing spots.

*Butterflies such as Swallowtail butterflies (in photo) will visit a variety of flowers including Bee Balm. Hummingbird and butterflies are attracted to **pink and red flowers**. In general, bees visit **blue, yellow and white flowers**. One good nectar flow sign is flower nectar dripping out of hive frames!*

DO YOU HAVE TO USE "ROUNDUP"?

Some large scale planting programs that assist landowners with free or discounted seeds either **require or highly recommend** the use of glyphosate products to clear the property before seeding. **The product use ensures** a better "take" on the planting in a shorter period of time, usually five years.

However, **landowners can pursue alternate methods** to prepare the property. Some of those will take more time and be more costly than using glyphosates.

Check with the planting program to identify what alternative options they will accept and weigh your options before deciding.

Scientific research continues to study how glyphosate products impact bees, from testing if it disorients young bees to whether it disrupts the bee's gut microorganisms.

SEED FARMERS VERSUS CROP FARMING

Pollination is all about helping plants set a good seed. Once a plant has healthy seeds, the seeds produce a food crop. Crop farmers and seed farmers are not after the same objective so sometimes their interests conflict.

- Crop farmers want pollinators visiting their fields and moving pollen for a higher crop yield, which includes **setting seeds that develop into fruits and nuts.**
- Seed farmers **don't want pollination taking away from the purity of the seed.** It makes the product less valuable and less effective for future growing seasons.
- Crop farmers **depend on good seed** to plant crops so they are both interdependent.
- As more land is developed into monoculture crops and seed production, **there are fewer landscapes** with the variety of pollen sources that maintain a healthy interdependent ecosystem.

*A honey bee visits one of my **pear trees** early spring, ensuring the fruit tree provides an excellent pear crop later in the season. One out of every three bites of healthy food are courtesy of bee pollination.*

*In late winter, bees **may raid bird feeders** to pick up pollen from cracked corn. Bees mix honey with pollen and store it in wax. Once fermented, beebread has a shiny glazed appearance.*

STARTING LIST OF MIDWEST BEE PLANTS

This is a starting list of plants you can add in the Midwest.
How many do you currently have on your property?

SPRING BLOOMERS

GARDEN PLANTS

- ☐ Blackberry *(Rubus allegheniensis)*
- ☐ Red Raspberry *(Rubus Idaeus)*
- ☐ Wild Strawberry *(Fragaria virginiana)*

TREES FOR BEES

- ☐ Witch Hazel *(Jan.-March)*
- ☐ Serviceberry *(March-May)*
- ☐ Willow *(Feb.-June)*
- ☐ Redbud *(March-April)*
- ☐ Red Maple *(Feb.-April)*
- ☐ Dogwood *(April)*

WOODY PLANTS

- ☐ Black Cherry *(Prunus serotine)*
- ☐ Box Elder *(Acer negundo)*
- ☐ Currants *(Ribes aureum, americanum, odoratum)*
- ☐ Black Locust *(Robinia pseudoacacia)*
- ☐ Honey Locust *(Gleditsia triacanthos)*
- ☐ Ninebark *(Physoxarpus opulifolius)*
- ☐ Northern Catalpa *(Catalpa speciose)*
- ☐ Wild Plum *(Prunus Americana)*
- ☐ Willow *(Salix spp)*

SUMMER BLOOMERS*

*Summer plants stop blooming when temperatures are 86°F
or higher for more than a solid week.*

GARDEN PLANTS

- ☐ **Anise Hyssop** (*Agastache foeniculum*)
- ☐ **Bee Balm** (*Monarda fistulosa*)
- ☐ **Cup Plant** (*Silphim perfoliatum*)
- ☐ **Milkweeds** (*Asclepias spp*)
- ☐ **Mountain Mint** (*Pycnanthemum spp*)
- ☐ **Purple Giant Hyssop** (*Agastache scrophulariifolia*)
- ☐ **Yarrow** (*Achillea millefolium var occidentalis*)

WOODY PLANTS

- ☐ **American Persimmon** (*Diospyros virginiana*)
- ☐ **Buttonbush** (*Cephalanthus occidentalis*)
- ☐ **Linden** (*Tillia spp*)
- ☐ **Ninebark** (*Physocarpus opulifolius*)
- ☐ **Sumac** (*Rhus spp*)

MORE MIDWEST TREES FOR BEES

- ☐ **Black Locust** (*May-June*)
- ☐ **Catalpa** (*May-June*)
- ☐ **Tulip Poplar** (*May-June*)
- ☐ **Basswood** (*June-July*)

FALL BLOOMERS*

Early Fall plants stop blooming when temperatures are 86°F or higher for more than a solid week.

GARDEN PLANTS

- ☐ **Asters** *(Symphyotrichum spp)*
- ☐ **Autumn Fire Sedum (***Sedum "Autumn Fire"*)
- ☐ **Autumn Joy Sedum** *(Sedum "Autumn Joy")*
- ☐ **Culvers Root** *(Veronicastrum virginicum)*
- ☐ **Goldenrod** *(Solidago spp***)**
- ☐ **Maximilian Sunflower** *(Helianthus maximiliani)*
- ☐ **Smartweed** *(Polygonum spp)*
- ☐ **Sneezeweed** *(Helenium autumnale)*
- ☐ **Sunflower** *(Helianthus spp)*

OTHER BLOOMERS: SAMPLE BEE FOOD LAWN PLANTS

- ☐ **Common Blue Violet** *(Viola sororia)*
- ☐ **Dandelion** *(Taraxacum officinale)*
- ☐ **Selfheal** *(Prunella vulgaris spp. Lanceolate)*
- ☐ **White Dutch Clover** *(Trifolum repens)*

SAMPLE AGRICULTURAL CROPS

- ☐ **Alfalfa**
- ☐ **Cover Crops** *(clovers, vetch)*
- ☐ **Fruit trees** *(apples, cherries, peaches, pears, plums)*
- ☐ **Melons and cucumbers**
- ☐ **Squash and pumpkins**
- ☐ **Berries** *(blackberries, raspberries, strawberries)*

☐ Sunflowers

☐ Field Peas

☐ Dry Beans

Corn (spring) and wheat (fall) are not bee food sources.

HOW TO PREVENT INSECTICIDE & PESTICIDE BEE DAMAGE

Not all insecticides affect bees the same. Some kill on direct contact; others pick up the chemicals through a plant's pollen. Your best approach is to **keep your bees away from chemicals if at all possible.**

One of the biggest challenges to bees in urban areas is the use of "Malathion" to manage mosquitoes. This product kills bees when bees land on the flowers that have been sprayed. **Monitor how your community is dealing with mosquito outbreaks** and make your needs known through your local governmental public comment sessions and open houses.

- If your state has a hive registration program, **register your hives** so applicators know where your hives are located.
- If you know applicators are working in your area, **talk to applicators** and make sure they do not spray directly in the area where your hives are located.
- Some products have to be applied to blooming plants to be effective. If you know where applicators will spray, **move your bees** if you can out of the range of the sprayed plants.
- If you can't move your bees, **use a water mist sprinkler** to keep bees in the hive or
- **Cover hives with netting** to keep bees close. They can still fly out of the hive but won't forage.
- **Wind breaks** can act as a drift barrier to reduce direct exposure to pesticide applications.
- **Work with your local applicators** to educate them about the impacts of their work on your bees.
- **Take an applicator training session** so you better understand how they should operate and apply the products they are using.
- **Notify your neighboring beekeepers** if you see an imminent issue developing so you can work together to get it resolved.
- Don't overlook the power of **sharing a jar of local honey** with your friendly applicator!

YOUR ROLE IN MAINTAINING HEALTHY ECOSYSTEMS

Pollinator conservation depends largely on private landowner decisions and land use practices. More than 90% of the land in Missouri, and **70% of land in the US, is in private hands.**

- **Plant micro clovers and bee lawns** instead of turf grass. The US has land equivalent to the size of Texas planted in turf grass, a plant that offers no redeeming value to pollinators.
- **Plant more native flowers, shrubs and trees**, they are part of your local interdependent ecosystems. Check with your local state conservation office for help in identifying best plants.
- **Learn to use companion plants** to discourage unwanted bugs instead of insecticides.
- **Keep your soil healthy.** Compost; mulch. Healthy soils produce healthy plants that feed our bees.
- **Do not apply pesticides.** Especially don't apply pesticides when plants are in bloom.

REMEMBER TO OFFER A WATER SOURCE

Honey bees depend on water sources to supplement their floral diet. Ensure that your honey bees have a continuous water source close to hives. Bees carry water back to hive to mix with food they make and to keep the hive cool.

- Bees prefer warm "dirty water."
- Add sticks, gravels and other **safe landing spots** in the water source so bees don't drown.
- The closer the better, and no farther than half a mile away from the home hive.

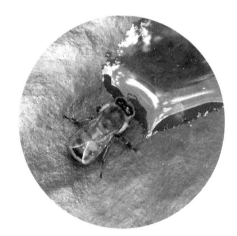

*Bees **need a nearby water source** to keep hive cool and to mix with food they make. They prefer warm dirty water with leaves and sticks that supplement minerals in the floral diet.*

WHO ARE YOU GOING TO CALL?

There are a variety of local, state and federal agencies available to help you.

Bee City USA and Campus USA

Bee City USA and Campus USA are programs that "foster ongoing dialogue in urban areas to raise awareness of the role pollinators play in our communities and what each of us can do to provide them with healthy habitat.

The Bee City USA program endorses a set of commitments, defined in a resolution, for creating sustainable pollinator habitats.

Incorporated cities, towns, counties and communities across America are invited to make these commitments and become certified as a Bee City USA affiliate." More details at **beecityusa.org**

Sample Land Management Resources

Missourians for Monarchs Find an Expert: Locate a Missouri Department of Conservation, Natural Resource Conservation Agency and US Fish and Wildlife representative in your county: **moformonarchs.org/find-an-expert**

Missourians for Monarchs planting guides to download: **bit.ly/MM-plant-guide**

Webinar Series: Past and future webinars on planting for pollinators and associated issues at **pollinator.org/webinars**

SAMPLE SEEDS, NATIVE SHRUBS, TREE SOURCES

Seed a Legacy Program Bee and Butterfly Habitat Fund

- **The Seed A Legacy Pollinator Habitat Program** is available for private, public and corporate lands in a 12-state US region critical to pollinator health and habitat needs. Applications are accepted for projects in the following states: Illinois, Indiana, Iowa, Kansas, Michigan, Minnesota, Missouri, Nebraska, North Dakota, Ohio, South Dakota, and Wisconsin. **bit.ly/SAL-program**
- **George O. White State Nursery**, Licking, MO: **bit.ly/GOW-nursery**

Missouri Botanical Garden Plant ID

Missouri Botanical Garden free online source to help you identify plants: **bit.ly/MBG-plant-i**

LEARN TO TRACK NATURE'S SIGNS *(Phenology)*

As a beekeeper, start to observe nature more closely to manage changes in nature that impact your bees.		
TIME OF YEAR	**ACTIVITY**	**NOTES**
March 20: Spring	Dandelions bloom. *What marks the start of nectar flow in your area? ie. When blackberries bloom.*	
June 20: Summer	*Flow ends with 86°F+ temperatures.* Bees raid hummingbird feeders.	
Sept. 20: Fall	Second nectar flow begins. *What indicates fall nectar flow? ie. Goldenrod in bloom; produces dirty-sock smelling honey.*	
Dec. 20: Winter	Days get longer, trigger queen egg laying.	

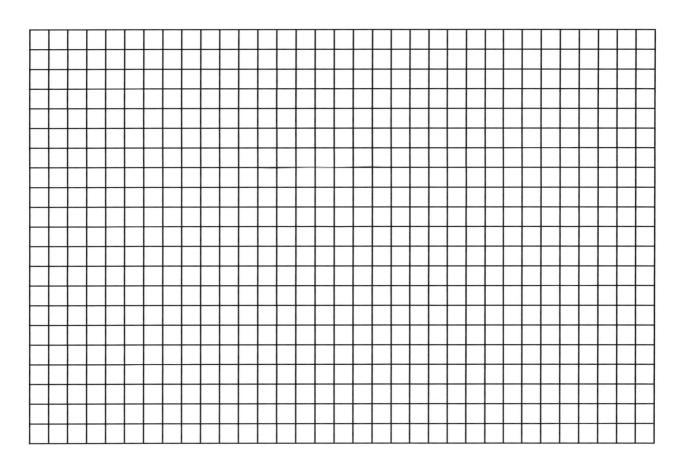

YOUR PROPERTY MAP

Pull out your favorite coloring pens and **draw your property** on this map with your house and major buildings, bee food sources and where you are planning to place your hives:

Notes:

_____

_____

Signage of nearby honey bee hives can be helpful to protect neighbors and delivery services.

WHAT TO CONSIDER WHEN LOCATING YOUR HIVES

Highly populated areas are not good hive candidate locations:

- How close will the proposed apiary location be to **schools, sidewalks, retail centers and ball fields**?
- Are there other beekeepers **within 5 miles** of your proposed location?

How close are foraging areas to:

- Honey bees **tend to stay close to home** if suitable forage is available nearby.
- Pollen **foragers work closer to the hive** and work faster than nectar gatherers.
- Uniform pollination is made possible by **distributing hives**, not keeping them bunched up in fewer locations.

HOW MANY HIVES? IN GENERAL, TWO HIVES PER ACRE

- Don't line hives up in close proximity. **Scatter hives across your property** with the most possible distance between them. Staggering hives and providing distance reduces the transmission of pests and diseases and discourages robbing.
- What are your **options to conceal** your hives?
- **How accessible** is your proposed hive location? How often will you visit the hives? Are they close enough you can visit them often? Do you have room for a sitting bench nearby?
- **What other considerations** do you think would be important?

_____

_____

_____

_____

POSSIBLE HIVE AND APIARY LOCATIONS

HOW MUCH LAND DO YOU HAVE AROUND YOUR CURRENT HOME?

Size	Wooden Stand
	Concrete Block
Alternate Site (s)	Repurposed Pallets
	Metal
	Other

Describe area under hives:

- ☐ *Concrete*
- ☐ *Grass*
- ☐ *Weeds*
- ☐ *Plastic*
- ☐ *Carpet*

Is this a floodplain?   ☐ Yes ☐ No ☐ I don't know

What will you be using for hive stands?

- ☐ *Wooden*
- ☐ *Stands*
- ☐ *Concrete*
- ☐ *Blocks*
- ☐ *Repurposed*
- ☐ *Pallets*
- ☐ *Metal*
- ☐ *Other:* _____

What seating is nearby so you can observe your hives?

_____

Other nearby property tenants:

- ☐ _Neighbors_
- ☐ _Cattle_
- ☐ _Goats_
- ☐ _Chickens_
- ☐ _Other:_____

Local laws restricting hive numbers and placement?

☐ Yes ☐ No ☐ I don't know

_____

GOOD TO KNOW
TIP

When setting up your hives, make sure **to include a nearby seating spot** so you can easily, and comfortably, watch your bees. You can re-purpose a pallet into a nice apiary bench.

Your Notes

_____

_____

_____

_____

_____

_____

_____

_____

_____

Your Notes

_____

_____

_____

_____

_____

_____

_____

_____

_____

CHAPTER 3

Beekeeping Basics

HOW MUCH IS THIS GOING TO COST?

It's one of the first questions prospective beekeepers ask. On the average, it's going to cost **$500-$1,000 to start** keeping honey bees, not counting the freezer.

Most of this cost is **for equipment you won't have to replace**, and other items that will last for several seasons. Bee suits, for example, will last a number of years before they need to be replaced. So will hive tools **if you can keep track of them.**

The freezer has become a more critical tool for pest control. Look for **a good used one.**

*Do you have room under your deck? Consider closing it in to easily make a **beekeeping equipment storage area.** You will be surprised at how quickly you will need a place to store everything.*

HOW MANY HIVES TO START?

Your best investment is to **start with two colonies.**

TWO COLONIES *(and a Nuc)*

- You will learn beekeeping basics faster by being able to compare the two colonies.
- If one colony is weaker than the other one, **you can also borrow resources** from your stronger colony.

As you work with your bees, you can also **get a nucleus colony (nuc) started** as a "back up" in case something goes wrong with your two colonies. A nuc is an easy way to hedge your initial investment.

ONE COLONY *(and a Nuc)*

If you choose to get one colony, definitely **plan on getting a backup nuc** established as soon as you can.

- Start a nucleus colony **to raise an extra queen** for when you need one.
- Sometimes queens are inadvertently killed in the first year of beekeeping by the new beekeeper **"rolling the queen"** as they quickly remove a frame of bees.
- Since you don't have another colony for comparison, plan to **spend time observing your bees** and comparing what you see with other beekeepers.

*When buying a nucleus box, **get the second nuc super,** too so you can safely feed bees inside. (This one has a nuc cover with a jar opening on the bottom cover so it needs a second box to protect the jar.)*

WHY A NUC

A nucleus colony is a **starter colony** with five frames.

- Two to three of the frames have brood and a laying queen; another frame has beebread and honey; the last frame has room for the queen bee to lay.

- When purchased in spring, they can **quickly expand** into a full colony.
- They provide the beginning beekeeper with a backup colony in case something happens with other colonies. They are **a "bank"** of brood frames and a queen.
- They are also less expensive than a full established colony.

When ordering nucs, ask supplier **if they want new frames** when you pick up the nucs. Some exchange occupied frames for new ones.

WHAT IS THE MAXIMUM NUMBER OF HIVES?

(Are you ready?) It depends. If you live in an urban area, the number of hives may be higher than living in a suburban or rural area.

In general, **two hives per backyard and two colonies per acre** is a general good rule, **depending on available foraging resources. Remember it takes 2 million flowers for bees to make one pound of honey.**

According to Dr. Tom Seeley, a natural bee colony **needs the following** in a year:

- **Nectar:** 264 lbs
- **Water:** 26.4 quarts
- **Pollen:** 44 lbs
- **Resin/Propolis:** 7 oz

If you are planning on bees for crop pollination, the number of **needed colonies will vary** depending on the crop.

*Regardless of where you place your hives, make sure you can **securely tie your hives** down in the event of bad weather. This is a telescoping hive lid with an inner cover.*

PLACING HONEY BEE HIVE(S) *Check List*

(Check all that apply)

- ☐ *Continuously blooming plants* during your growing season.
- ☐ *Full sun* away from prevailing winds.
- ☐ Hive **entrances facing south/southeast.**
- ☐ Two or more hives **not lined in a row** and as far apart as possible.
- ☐ Hives sit at least 12 inches above ground.
- ☐ *Hives level from side to side* and back to front to allow for even comb building.
- ☐ Hives tilted forward a smidge to allow water inside to run off.
- ☐ Can you *daily get to hives* even if ground is soggy?
- ☐ Do you have **seating observation area close to hives?**

How will you **secure hive lids?**	☐ Rocks ☐ Bricks ☐ Hooks ☐ Bungee Cords ☐ Other: _____
Water source within ½ mile of potential hive location(s)	☐ Bird bath ☐ Pond ☐ Swimming Pool ☐ Mud Puddles ☐ Other: _____

Do **pets and children have easy access** to the hives?

_____

Are hives protected from neighbors/curious visitors?

_____

GOOD THINGS TO CONSIDER AS YOU BEGIN BEEKEEPING

Storage Space

It's one thing to find room to store a few supers when you're starting. When the numbers start hitting double digits, then **it's time for either an intervention or adding a wing to your house.** By this point you will be wondering if you will ever get your car back in your garage.

The good news is:
- **Most hive boxes can be stacked** for storage.
- **Wax frames can be stored** in large plastic containers with ParaMoth™ Crystals (para-Dichlorobenzene™) in a warm dry space to protect wax for use the following year. Do not use moth balls (naphthalene).
- You can **store empty hive boxes outside over winter.**

Make Your Own

New beekeepers who assemble their first beehives learn more than those who purchase their hives already assembled. **Some home-assembled woodenware** can be superior to "pre-fab" equipment. The constructing beekeeper has the opportunity to use better quality fasteners and ensure that all joints on boxes and frames are properly glued.

Find an experienced beekeeper to show you how to correctly assemble frames. It takes both glue and a fastener of some sort; nails or brads are best.

A new frame is very light. Once it gets honey-filled wax, **a medium super frame can weigh 3-5 lbs.**

Have Extra On Hand

Plan on having **at least another full hive on hand;** bees don't wait for you to place an equipment order.

If you need something quickly, **borrow from another beekeeper.**

Replace what you borrowed with your incoming equipment or order what you borrowed.

Dedicated Freezer

Freezing frames for at least 48 hours is the preferred choice for killing small hive beetles and wax moth larvae. Be careful, however, some family members **take issue**

seeing what appears to be specks of rice, and are frozen small hive beetle larvae, in their frozen ice cream.

Get a good used freezer. It will come in handy and could save your marriage.

Label Containers

Beekeeping supplies have a tendency to morph into the refrigerator, especially if you make your own small hive beetle lure.

Remember to **label your jars** so they are not mistaken for an exotic tea. No, **you don't want to sample small hive beetle lure,** even by accident. Allowing a family member to do so could be grounds for something even uglier. 'Just sayin.'

Shadow Someone

Some of the best beekeepers I know picked up a bee suit and hive tool and started their beekeeping journey by asking to **shadow practicing beekeepers.**

They worked hives sometimes for a year before they purchased equipment and bees. They undoubtedly picked up good tips and were better prepared to make decisions.

The most important thing they learned was **how to lose their fear of being around bees.**

Involve Family

If there is a family member who may be interested in beekeeping, **get them involved**.

Between adults and children, adults can be more scared of bees than young children. They also tend to have better eyesight and can see those tiny eggs the queen lays, that can come in quite handy!

Take It Slow

When starting, there is a tendency to want to get in quick and get out. Not a bad idea but when you are starting, you need to first **learn to do things slowly.**

Rapid **arm movements threaten bees.**

They also **don't like loud noises** and **banging on their home walls.** (Would you?)

TYPES OF HONEY BEE HIVES

When I started beekeeping in 2010, the Langstroth hive was the only hive beekeepers around me had and discussed. With the increase in beekeeping interest, today's beginning beekeeper has more choices, including the easier-to-lift 8 frame hives. To save back strain, several beekeeping friends are also raising bees in long or horizontal hives, which can either be top bar or use Langstroth frames.

The following is a **list of popular hives** and their good and challenging points:

TYPES OF POPULAR HONEYBEE HIVES

TYPE	ADVANTAGES	DISADVANTAGES
Langstroth	• Most common in USA • Three sizes (deep, medium and shallow) • Two widths (10 and 8 frames) • One person to add boxes. • Moveable frames • Bee space • Easy to harvest honey • Easy to manage	• Can get tall. • Can get heavy but customizable. • Although same box sizes they are not all constructed the same.
Dadant Hive	• Standard hive outside US, close second to most popular hive.	• Hard to get parts.
Top Bar or Horizontal Long Hive	• Single long box on legs, no need to mow around hive. • Doesn't require bending beekeeper's back to manage frames.	• No foundation. • More prone to abscond. • Difficult to harvest honey; bees have to rebuild comb. • Cross comb can be a problem. • More difficult to survive and control *Varroa* mites and harder to successfully over winter.

Warre	• Non-Standard sizes. • Less availability of equipment. • Similar to Langstroth but has foundationless issues like top bar.	• Heavy to lift; two person job to add boxes loaded from the bottom. • Difficult to remove frames for inspection.
Flow Hive	• Easy to extract honey if temperatures are conducive. • Flow Hive frame sets supplement the remaining space with standard Langstroth frames.	• Expense. • Hard to manage: must keep frames from binding. • Doesn't substitute for managing bees.
Skep	• Traditional symbol of beekeeping, this is the rounded wicker hive seen in historical references. It is currently popular in beekeeping logos and illustrations.	• Because it does not have removable frames, it is not considered a legal way in the US to keep honey bees.

Horizontal hives can use regular deep frames or foundationless top bars. These popular hives require **regular monitoring to guide colony expansion.** *They can be challenging to move. They are also easier on beekeeper's back.*

WHY START WITH A LANGSTROTH

When beginning to keep bees, the most critical part is to learn how to **gently handle your bees.** That takes practice and spending quality time with your colonies. You will tend to do that **if the hive is easier to access and manage. The Langstroth hive** has several advantages:

- It is currently the **most widely-used hive style** in the US.
- **Has removable frames** for easy management.
- **Hive parts are readily available** at most beekeeping suppliers and from other helpful beekeepers.
- Beginning beekeepers will be able to **more readily follow class instructions** since the Langstroth is used as the foundation of the lessons.
- **Reading your bees, spotting problems with brood and diseases, and learning how to correct them** are critical in your first few years. **Once you get an understanding** of the honey bee life cycle and get basic management techniques down, **you can experiment** with other bee hive forms.

NOTE: Once you decide on a hive body supplier, **stick with that supplier. Hive sizes vary with manufacturers.**

LANGSTROTH HIVE OPTIONS

There are two basic hive sizes: 10 frame and 8 frame hives. The smaller, 8 frame hives have become increasingly popular because they are kinder on a beekeeper's back.

Either way, both sizes have the following "drawers" as part of each hive:

- **Deeps.** Usually used as part of the brood chamber, where the queen lays eggs.
- **Mediums or Illinois.** Also referred to as supers depending on how they are being used in the hive.
- **Shallows.** Not used much anymore, these small supers were used exclusively for honey collecting.

HIVE BODY SIZES

It may be easy to move hive equipment when you first start. When that hive is full of honey, though, **it becomes a feat of strength** to move the boxes. Take "honey weight' into consideration as you **decide what hive size to get.** A beekeeping friend actually started working out to improve her upper arm strength so she could more easily move hive boxes. *(On the other hand, you are getting a workout without ever setting foot in a gym.)*

You can provide bees a home with **all deeps or all medium boxes.** Adjust how and when you provide bees more room depending on what hive box size you choose.

More new beekeepers are choosing the **8-frame medium hives** today because **they are lighter** when full of honey.

Shallow boxes are exclusively used for honey collecting. To cut down on different frame sizes, most beekeepers today use medium supers for honey collecting instead of shallows.

Although hive box sizes should be the same, **hive boxes are not easily interchangeable** between manufacturers. Once you decide on what supplier you want to use for your hive boxes, **stick with that supplier.** Your hive boxes will fit together better.

Equipment suppliers offer a **hive carrier transport lifter** *that - not may - WILL save straining your back. It takes two people to use it but it makes moving hives safer. (Photo by Lorri Thurman)*

HIVE BODY SIZES AND WEIGHT WITH HONEY

Beekeepers refer to hive bodies by how bees use them. Here is a quick guide to explain some of the more common terms used for hive boxes, their height and width, and approximate *honey weight when full of honey.

NAME	WEIGHT	SIZE	BASIC USE
Deep 10 frame	90-100 lbs	9⅝ inches high **16¼ inches wide** 19⅞ inches long	The brood chamber, where bees store food, raise bees and queen lays.
Deep 8 frame	70-80 lbs	9⅝ inches high **14 inches wide** 19⅞ inches long	Two deeps, and a deep and one medium, often make up the brood chamber for winter.
Medium 10 frame	50-60 lbs	**16½ inches wide** 6⅝ inches high 19⅞ inches long	Also called Super, Illinois, Box. Can be used to extend brood chamber and as honey-collecting boxes.
Medium 8 frame	40-50 lbs	**14 inches wide** 6⅝ inches high 19⅞ inches long	Three mediums can also be a brood chamber equivalent to two deeps.
Shallow 10 frame	30-40 lbs	**16¼ inches wide** 5¹¹⁄₁₆ inches high 19⅞ inches long	Formerly used for honey-collecting, now mediums fill in for them. Still available for beekeepers who struggle with box weight.
Shallow 8 frame	20-30 lbs	**14 inches wide** 5¹¹⁄₁₆ inches high 19⅞ inches long	
Deep 5 frame nuc	Weight Varies	**11½ inches high** 9¼ inches wide 19⅞ inches long	Can house both deep and medium frames. If you have to choose, buy a deep nuc.
Medium 5 frame nuc	Weight Varies	**6⁹⁄₁₆ inches high** 9¼ inches wide 19⅞ inches long	Lighter to carry than a deep nuc box.

PARTS OF A BASIC LANGSTROTH HIVE

*The Langstroth hive is the **current US traditional beekeeping hive** with removable frames, a requirement in many US states that regulate beekeeping.*

BOTTOM BOARDS

- ☐ Solid bottom board
- ☐ Screened bottom board
- ☐ Screened bottom board with solid inserts

HIVE LIDS/COVERS/INNER COVERS

- ☐ Telescoping hive lid
- ☐ Migratory hive lid
- ☐ Solid inner covers
- ☐ Screened inner covers
- ☐ Feeding Shims

ENTRANCE REDUCERS

- ☐ Single
- ☐ Reversible
- ☐ Mouse guards
- ☐ Boardman feeders
- ☐ Pollen trap
- ☐ Other: _____

HIVE FRAMES

- ☐ Medium wooden frames with wax foundation
- ☐ Medium black plastic frames
- ☐ Medium waxed plastic frames
- ☐ Medium empty no foundation frames
- ☐ Green drone frames
- ☐ Deep wood frames w/wax foundation
- ☐ Deep black plastic frames
- ☐ Deep waxed plastic frames
- ☐ Deep empty frames
- ☐ Deep green drone frames
- ☐ Shallow honey frames
- ☐ Either wood foundation or plastic frames. Not easily available due to lack of use.

FRAME HOLDERS

- ☐ Attaches to hive box side so frames can be held while colony is inspected.

NUCLEUS BOX

- ☐ Holds 5 frames and is used to start a new colony.
- ☐ Also available in less than 5 frame sizes; minimum of 2 frames.

Sample 10 Frame Bee Hive *at my Missouri limestone hillside apiary. This was one of my two first bee colonies sold to me as used equipment. I caulked and repainted it to extend the hive body life. From left, going up and around, on next page:*

SAMPLE 10 FRAME LANGSTROTH BEE HIVE DETAILS

☐ Telescoping cover	Nice flat top surface handy for placing equipment; using as a temporary bottom board when inspecting.
☐ Frame holder	Safely keeps bee-filled frames as you're inspecting. You can also easily make one—really!
☐ Medium frame with wax-covered foundation	Bees will more readily pull wax from a wax and wax-covered foundation.
☐ Screened or solid inner cover	Good for winter; can be replaced with a screened inner cover in summer for better ventilation.
☐ Smoker	A beekeeper's best friend; can be a challenge to light.
☐ Muslin kitchen towels	Nice option for keeping bees calm without smoke.
☐ Hive strap	Easy-to-use strap to keep hive together.
☐ Painted hive	Add geometric designs so bees can easily find their way home.
☐ Entrance reducer	To help guard bees keep unwanted visitors out.
☐ Screened or solid bottom board	The bottom of the hive brood box.
☐ Narrow concrete block	To better monitor bees coming out of or being dragged out of hive.

*When starting, you can either buy assembled frames with foundation or assemble your own frames using both nails and glue, **then adding foundation.** Black foundation makes seeing eggs easier. **Start with frames with foundation,** then learn how to manage foundationless frames.*

FRAMES, FRAMES, AND MORE FRAMES!

In addition to the parts of a hive, you will need to **decide what kind of frames and foundation** you will offer your bees.

If your bees are not taking to a frame, spray the frame with 1 to 1 sugar syrup to encourage frame use. Monitor the frame; if the bees are still not using the frame, replace it.

Reused wax comb will get darker, stained by larvae cocoons and excrement. Pesticides accumulate in the wax comb so plan on replacing used dark frames every 2-3 years or so.

*A wind storm knocked this hive over in my southern apiary. Once upright again, **the colony was fine** including the queen.*

WHAT IF IT ALL FALLS OVER?

There are a lot of reasons why a hive may fall over: it's not level, rain made the soil underneath soft, wildlife visited and decided to get a closer look.

Weather can also impact a hive, which is one reason you will often find experienced beekeepers **keeping bricks and rocks** on top of their hives. They want to make sure the lid stays on.

If your hive happens to fall over, **take a deep breath:**

- Suit up and carefully note what may have happened.
- Place the inner cover over the spilled frames if you can reach them and use it to gently hold frames in as you turn the super upright.
- If you can't, slowly turn the super upright and adjust frames.
- You may injure some bees and possibly the queen so go slowly and gently.
- Place the supers in the original order.
- Add the inner cover, lid and let the bees settle back in.
- After a week, check for any sign of egg-laying. That will tell you the queen survived.

BURR COMB

- Bees may deposit small wax comb pieces on frame tops and bottom.

Hairpins are a good substitute if you don't have, or run out of, foundation support pins. (Remember to replace them with new ones or the original hairpin owner may not be happy!)

TYPES OF LANGSTROTH HIVE FRAMES AND FOUNDATION

FRAME	PROS	CONS
All plastic foundation	• Long lasting. • Easy to clean. • Spin well in extractors.	• Bees may not use. • Bees may use it if nothing else available. • Needs re-waxing.
All plastic black foundation	• Easy to see eggs. • Long lasting. • Easy to clean. • Spins well in extractors.	• Bees may not use. • Bees may use it if nothing else available. • Needs re-waxing.
Wood frame with yellow plastic foundation	• Easy to replace foundation. • Spins well in extractors.	• May need re-waxing.
Wood frame with black plastic foundation	• Easy to see eggs. • Easy to replace foundation.	
Wood frame with all wax foundation	• Bees love!	• Delicate for honey extracting. • Needs support. • Wiring. • More time consuming to refurbish.
Frames with gutters at the top and sides		• Excellent small hive beetle larvae nurseries. • Don't buy. • Minimize use if given. Replace as soon as possible.

HOW TO IDENTIFY YOUR HIVES

When bees return home with their cargo, they need **a way to identify which hive is home.** Those all-white painted hives placed close together in commercial beekeeping operations lose an average of 35% of their bees to 'drifting," or bees ending up in the closest hive they land on.

The following are suggested ways to help bees identify home, with some options included for the benefit of the beekeeper.

*Hives can be **painted with different colors** and geometric designs to help bees find home when they return from foraging.*

PAINT COLORS

- You can get **interior latex sample paints** at local home and garden centers that will work well. Home and garden centers also have **discarded discounted latex paints both latex interior and exterior.**

- Some beekeepers have **family members or grade schools students** paint their hive bodies.

- **Use different light paint colors.** Don't use dark colors, bees see blacks and dark browns as threats.

*Paint each **super with different designs** so that you can easily interchange the boxes without breaking up the paint design.*

BY NUMBERS

- You can **paint and apply** numerical numbers somewhere on your hive. If you paint them boldly on fronts, your bees will use the numbers geometric shapes as navigational guides.

- **Also paint the numbers on the hive backs** so you can easily see them as you approach the hive. **Beekeepers should approach hives from the back,** not from the front. Bees use the front to enter and leave the hive. Most beekeepers can also use numbers as navigational guides.

BY NAME

- **Give your colony a name** based on the hive color and/or design. Use that name to refer to the colony living in that hive in your records.

- Sorry, your bees won't respond to the name you give the hive (but wouldn't that be fun!)

NAME THE QUEEN BEES

- Each queen is unique and **can be named to help YOU identify the colony.**

- When the queen is superseded you decide if you want to keep the first queen name for the hive or give the new queen a new name. **Do what works best for your record keeping.**

NAME HIVES AFTER FAMILY

- Naming hives **after family members** can get the family interested and involved in beekeeping.

- **However.** Using the family member names as a short cut can create some confusion and, better yet, giggling in public, especially when the discussion turns to "Steve swarmed today" and "Rachel stopped laying."

- **Honey Possessiveness.** "Some" (of my) family members have been known to insist that they want "only" the honey from **"their" hive because it has their name.** We won't get into the claims that one honey is better than the other. (Silly brothers!)

PAINTING AND DECORATING
HONEY BEE HIVE OPTIONS

WHAT	TIPS
☐ *Need primer?*	Primer may help cut down on a second color coat.
☐ *Use Latex paint*	Don't paint the inside of hive bodies. Allow to fully dry before using.
☐ *Painting all hives white*	Make each hive unique with paint and geometric designs so bees don't drift into other homes. To get different colors, use interior Latex paint sample colors.
☐ *Different Geometric Hive Entrance Designs*	Unique designs help bees identify and return to their original hive.
☐ *Painted designs on different supers*	Nice way to give a hive personality. Keep the full design on each box so the boxes are easily interchangeable.
☐ *Frames, inner covers painted?*	No, wood frames and inner covers go inside the hive and are left natural.
☐ *Painting bottom boards*	You can paint bottom boards to help the wood last longer.
☐ *Can you paint wood with polyurethane?*	There are bee safe products on the market that are better choices.
☐ *Can hive bodies be dipped in wax?*	Yes. See if there is a commercial beekeeper who can do that for you for a fee.

☐ *Do I have to paint my hive?*	If your hive is made of wood, painting will help preserve it.
☐ *Do I paint my hive if it is made out of plastic?*	No. If you have two or more hives, you may want to add some way to identify it such as an identifying number or different geometric designs at the hive fronts.

OTHER HELPFUL HINTS

If you use hive numbers, **place on both front and back** so bees can see the geometric designs to find home and beekeeper can easily identify the hive.

Paint dries slower in winter than summer. If **painting in winter, allow a good couple of months** for paint to dry.

Paint inside of hive covers white to more easily see small hive beetles and *Varroa* when you place hive boxes on them. Small hive beetles don't like sun and will move around the inside cover when exposed to sun.

Varroa mites will be easier to see against a white background.

GOOD TO KNOW

TIP

*You can **use medium frames in deep hive bodies**. Bees will draw or build comb along frame bottoms to fill empty space.*

Your Notes

_____

_____

_____

_____

_____

_____

_____

_____

_____

CHAPTER 4

Beginning Beekeeping Equipment

*A local journalist meets a worker honey bee in my apiary **for the very first time!***

THE BEST-DRESSED BEEKEEPER BEE SUIT OPTIONS

- **Full bee suit.** Then as you become more comfortable with your bees, graduate to **beekeeping jacket** with jeans.
- Don't depend on disposable painter's suits for beekeeping. As your **colony grows, the less effective the painter's suit** will be.

BEEKEEPING GLOVE OPTIONS

- **Cowhide:** medium thick, best sting protection.
- **Goatskin:** lighter than cowhide, more dexterity; less sting protection.
- **Nitrile:** best dexterity. Considered disposable, high quality nitrile gloves can often be used several times before they have to be replaced.

HONEY BEE FASHIONISTAS - *NOT!*

Honey bees **do not like:**

- **Dark clothing** (dark brown, black)
- **Dark wool – well, anything wool**
- **Most scents and perfumes**
- Perfumed hair products
- Perfumed body products
- Especially "Eau de Banana"; banana scent simulates the bee's danger pheromone. **Don't eat a banana before visiting bees.**

WHEN PREPARING TO VISIT YOUR HIVES

- **Wear protective gear** including suit and gloves.
- If wearing a bee jacket, **wear jeans or thick but light-colored pants.**
- **Tuck pants legs inside white cotton socks** to keep bees from flying up your legs. No dark wool socks.
- **Tie your long hair back to keep it out of your eyes.** Note: There are no such thing as "good hair days" when spending a day in your apiary.
- **Approach the hives from the back, not the front.** You don't want to get in the way of your bees flying in and out. (And no point in making the guard bees job easier, is there?)

WHEN WORKING IN YOUR HIVE(S)

- Make sure your smoker is properly lit and producing a **good white smoke.**
- **Take a deep breath. No need to be "scared to death."**
- Approach hive **quietly.**
- **Work slowly and deliberately.** No fast movements; bees will read fast hand movements as a threat.
- **Take notes/photos** for review later.
- **If bees attack you or your gloves,** gently smoke sting site immediately to reduce/mask pheromone. Yes, smoke your legs and arms with a bee suit on.
- If stung, you can also **dust sting area with mud or talcum powder** to mask attack pheromone.
- **Observe.** Bees should be going about their business. **If bees are watching you,** they may be getting ready to sting. Best to close up and go back later.

- **Sticky notes** inside hive lids will help you remember what needs to be done in your next visit.
- After use, **clean your hive tool. Use rubbing alcohol or place hive tool in smoldering smoker.** Be careful when removing hive tool, it may be hot.

Notes:

_____

_____

_____

WHEN VISITING OTHER APIARIES

- Wear protective gear including suit and gloves. Those bees don't know you as they do their beekeeper.
- Clean hive tool before using between hives.
- Clean hive tool again before using back at your hives.

Notes:

_____

_____

_____

AFTER SEVERAL APIARY VISITS *(Especially during hot weather)*

- **Wash your bee suit and gloves.** Bees, and dear ones who used to be close to you, not may—**WILL**—object if your bee suit is so dirty it can stand on its own.

Remember, **bees are also guided by scent!**

HOW TO WASH YOUR BEE SUIT

Follow bee suit washing directions. If you have lost bee suit washing directions and think you can **toss it into your washer, don't!**

- **Remove bee suit hood.** Hand wash and allow the bee suit hood to drip dry. (Hang over shower head.)
- Wash bee suit in cold water **without scented products.**

- Allow to drip dry or dry on cool dryer setting.
- Enjoy your new white bee suit when you first get it. **It will become permanently soiled and stained as you work your bees.** Don't fret over it, that's another mark of an experienced beekeeper!

Notes:

_____

_____

_____

HOW TO WASH YOUR LEATHER GLOVES

- **Wash gloves gently** with hand dishwashing soap and warm water. This should remove honey, wax, and propolis, a "glue" bees make from tree resin.
- **Use a cleaning solution on the tougher spots** such as chlorine water to disinfect leather and break up wax and propolis. Alcohol may break down leather; use quickly and sparingly.
- **Rinse gloves thoroughly.**
- **Hang to dry.**
- While still slightly wet, **treat the dry leather with vegetable oil** (not olive oil, it is poisonous to bees.

Notes:

_____

_____

_____

*"Beekeeping Lingerie" also known as a bug baffle insect shirt is a lightweight jacket made out of mosquito netting. It is popular for swarm catching and light protection visiting other apiaries. This will **not substitute** for a beekeeping suit. Buy the netting only as an extra.*

BEEN THERE, DONE THAT - SUIT UP WITH QUALITY PROTECTIVE EQUIPMENT

- It will last you for years and **keep you safe.**
- **Over time,** quality protective equipment will be **a less expensive investment.**
- **Painters pants and suits will protect you when your hives are small;** they are not adequate protection when your colony is established.

SCARED TO DEATH

- Yes, that about **sums it up** when you **first open your hives.**
- **Take a deep breath.** It will get easier.
- Take it **slow.**

Working with your bees is the **best way to learn.** Pay attention; your bees will let you know how you are doing.

BUT MY BEES ARE GENTLE

Uh-huh. Well, when you are starting, your colonies are small in terms of bee numbers and may seem quite easy to manage.

As they grow, they will **become more defensive** of their home. You may not recognize the nice gentle bees you had your first year so:

- **Get used to wearing your protective gear at all times!**

GLOVES OR NO GLOVES

- **Start out** with leather gloves.
- As you develop a **slow, methodical technique** of inspecting your honey bees in good weather, **you can transition** to working your bees with nitrile gloves or no gloves.
- Always **keep a pair of gloves handy,** just in case.
- **Smoke your hands;** that will mask your scent.
- You will **learn when gloveless beekeeping is possible,** and downright enjoyable, and when it's not. Bees are great teachers.

BEE BAIT

"Bee Bait" is what one of our club spouses calls herself. You may think you are going into beekeeping all alone. The truth is you may start enticing family members and friends to join you in the bee yard; it sure makes moving a hive easier. However. Try to explain that to a spouse running around the yard with angry bees caught in his/her hair.

- **Buy them a bee jacket and gloves.**
- **Introduce them slowly** to the whole experience.
- **Kids in general** have less fear of working with bees than adults.
- **Letting them taste** their first piece of honey-filled wax comb is a pretty nice way to start.
- **Thank them** for helping you!

*Plan on involving family members. **Get them protective equipment** so their experience working with you is a pleasant one. Here my gardening buddy Tom Miller works with a tiny beginning beekeeper.*

HAVE A PLAN

- Before opening your hives, **have a plan** for what you intend to do.
- **Work your plan.**
- **Disturb your colonies** as little as possible.
- If you observe something you need to address, **consider whether now or another time** is better.
- If another time, **make a note** so you won't forget.

DON'T WAIT

- If you know you need to work your bees, **don't put it off.**
- **Bees will not wait** on your schedule.
- If you see queen cells at the bottom of frames looking like long peanut shells,

those are swarm cells. **Manage those cells.** You can divide the colony into two by making "a split" or make a nuc with those swarm cells. If not, you may loose bees every time a swarm cell ecloses with a new queen bee.

CHECK FRAME BOTTOMS FOR QUEEN SWARM CELLS.

Worker bees build **three kinds of queen cells;** swarm cells, usually on the bottom of frames; supercedure cells, typically in the frame center and emergency queen-raising cells. As you begin beekeeping, **check the bottom of frames for swarm cells.**

*Check **the bottom of frames for swarm cells.** If the cell has white royal jelly in it, the bees are raising a queen. Get ready to put the new queen cell(s) to good use!*

KEEP IT LEVEL

There's level and then there is **beekeeping level.**

When setting up your hives, make sure hives are level as in even to the ground. They should also be **slightly tilted down** at the front to prevent water from sitting inside the hive.

*Hives get heavier as the season unfolds. **Make sure they are safe and level** when you start and periodically check that they remain level. You also want a slight tilt downward at the front in case water gets in. Bees die from moisture, not cold.*

*Keep a small flashlight handy. The flashlight will help you to **easily spot eggs and larvae** in a frame.*

I DON'T WANT TO KILL A BEE

No one does. **But you will.**

- **Work slowly.**
- Use a **soft bee brush or large feather** to gently move bees and prevent crushing.

Think two steps ahead so what you do minimizes squishing them.

A TISKET, A BASKET

Think through how you will carry your beekeeping equipment to your hives. A woven basket and 5-gallon paint bucket can be handy.

Add those items that **you may need** to save yourself a trip back to your beekeeping storage area.

Use something that you can **easily manage.**

Personal Fashion Tip: Try to remember to **take your pants legs out of your socks** before going out in public. Not a deal breaker but you may find people smiling a lot more at you. **Smile back,** you will realize what happened later as you are taking off your bee *suit.*

*This is my hive inspection basket. It holds basic hive inspecting necessities from an extra bungee cord to my gloves and extra hive tool. **See the level?***

*My Bee Buddy David, left, helps me inspect one of my younger colonies. He is wearing a **full bee suit with the smaller hood** (aka fencing veil look alike.) I am wearing a half jacket over a t-shirt with jeans. My hood is the rounded shape, giving me better visibility. **Try on both to see which one you prefer.***

BEGINNING BEEKEEPER EQUIPMENT CHECK LIST

Beginning costs vary *depending on how much you buy. Pick up an equipment catalog to see photos and note pricing.*

- ☐ **Hive tool** (at least 2 for when you misplace one. Guaranteed!)

- ☐ **Beekeeping jacket with veil** or full suit with veil. Sleeve or pocket for hive tool is very handy.

- ☐ **Beekeeping gloves**

- ☐ **Frame rest**

- ☐ **Smoker** (with inside smoker tray)

- ☐ **Smoker fuels**

- ☐ **Long matches or long handled fire lighter.**

- ☐ **Cork or small stick** that fits smoker spout.

- ☐ **Muslin kitchen towels** to use to inspect hives without smoke.

- ☐ **Queen catcher;** to safely secure queen without hurting her.

- ☐ **Magnifying glass** to see 1 to 3-day old eggs.

- ☐ **Bee brush** or **turkey wing feather** to gently brush bees off.

- ☐ **Sticky notes** for tracking hive to do items during your next visit.

- ☐ **Antihistamine** (for sting reaction management)

- ☐ **Beekeeper's Diary** with inspection records.

- ☐ **Camera** for easy documentation.

- ☐ **Spray bottle** (for using later with 1:1 sugar syrup to coat the foundation frames).

- ☐ **Sugar syrup** pre-made for supplemental feeding, as needed.

- ☐ **Reusable small hive beetle traps.**

- ☐ **Distilled apple cider vinegar** and **mineral oil** to use in small hive beetle traps.

- ☐ **Small flashlight.** To illuminate eggs in frame wax so they're visible.

- ☐ **Auto-injector** (optional) like Epipen® or similar product in event of allergic reaction to bee sting.

- ☐ **Food grade essential oils** or **oil mixture additive** for bee health.

- ☐ **Deep nucleus box** so that it can also be used with medium frames.

- ☐ **Phone** (optional) to videotape and make notes provided you don't easily misplace it. If so, leave it safely at home!

Entrance reducers are like shoes, you can find them in a variety of styles and sizes. You can also use a 1x1 cut to size leaving a small open entrance at the corner.

DON'T FORGET ENTRANCE REDUCERS

When buying hive equipment, it's easy to forget about **entrance reducers.** These handy little pieces of wood close down a hive entrance to several sizes, from a strip of 5-inches to a two-bee space. **The entrance reducers are handy to have** for those new colonies that can use a little help guarding their resources.

Some beginning beekeeping kits with a complete hive include an entrance reducer. When buying a hive, you need to **order an entrance reducer as a separate item.**

To keep unwanted visitors out such as mice, there are also **mouse guards,** entrance reducers that allow bees in and keeps other visitors out.

Easy to make **homemade entrance reducers** can be found at your local hardware store. **Corner beading,** cut down to size, makes handy entrance reducers. Attach with stick pins. (Comes in handy when you forget to order one, too!)

THE SMOKER: A BEEKEEPER'S BEST FRIEND

Of all of the things you may learn from beekeeping, **making a fire in basically a soup can** may be the skill you will use in other aspects of your life; say stranded on a desert island, or lost in the woods. On the other hand, **as a beekeeper it is one of the more difficult and frustrating skills to develop**. It takes time, and practice, to get this right.

My first smoker, purchased quite used, some say it's an antique - still going strong with a little help of a homemade bottom tray.

Luckily, there is **an alternative way** to work your bees most of the time **without smoke.**

WHAT DOES SMOKE DO TO BEES

You may hear a **number of different reasons** why beekeepers use smoke.

- **Smoke masks the alarm pheromone** guard bees release when they think they are under attack. Bees are confused so they don't gather forces to quickly communicate.
- The smoke also **distracts bees.** They will concentrate on gorging on honey in case they need to abandon the hive. **As opposed to** paying close up attention to visiting beekeeper.

WHAT YOU NEED TO USE A SMOKER

Besides patience as you learn the art, and science of starting a smoker, you will need the removable inside smoker bottom tray. If you don't have one, **you won't be able to start, let alone maintain,** a fire. You need oxygen to move through your smoker fuel to start, and keep, a fire going.

New smokers come with a bottom tray. Used smokers may have burned theirs out so you will need to add one. You can have a handy welder make one for you or you can use #8 hardware cloth folded over several **times to hold** the fuel off the bottom.

1. Dry smoker **fuel examples:**

   - Small dry sticks
   - Cedar shavings used for pet bedding
   - Dry leaves
   - Crushed corn cobs commonly sold as animal bedding
   - Non synthetic burlap
   - Wood shavings
   - Cow patties

A smoker with a removable inside bottom tray to hold the smoker fuel off the smoker bottom. If you buy a used smoker, you may not have one so you will need to make one.

2. Not recommended as smoker fuel:

   - **Straw, hay, grass:** possible insecticides
   - **Denim:** includes blue dye
   - **Burlap:** some have plastics in the blend

3. Often recommended as smoker fuel but not good to use in large quantities, **pine needles**. Some research suggests pine needles leave an undesirable toxic oily coating on bees.

4. **Smoker starter pellets.** Available through beekeeping equipment suppliers. You can also make some with pinecones with an attached wick dipped in wax.

5. **Long handled matches and small lighter.** Although some demonstrations have the beekeeper using a large butane torch, that is overkill and possibly dangerous to the beekeeper. Keep things safe!

6. **Wax-covered cheesecloth.** If you use cheesecloth to render wax, you can cut up pieces of the dried wax-covered cheesecloth to use as a fire starter.

7. **Safe surface to place the lit smoker** such as a metal bucket. Examples of places **not to place a lit smoker:**

   - **Straw bales**
   - **Plastic surfaces**
   - **Dry grass**
   - **Un-level areas.**
   - **Your foot. That smoker is hot!**

8. **Cork or stick the width of the smoker opening.** Cork will plug spout and put the fire out.

9. **Do NOT use a smoker when it is windy.** You may **easily get a fire started** if the smoker falls over in dry grass. (You shouldn't be out in your hives on a windy day, anyway!)

HOW TO LIGHT YOUR SMOKER

When **starting your smoker**, your goal is to have **a cool, white smoke.** Anything hotter will burn your honey bees wings and antenna.

Before starting, gather the materials you plan to use.

1. Remove any remains from the last time you used your smoker. You can also clean your smoker when you finish your inspections and start with an empty smoker.

2. **Add a fire starter** to an empty smoker chamber bottom **shredded cardboard, wadded paper, pine cones and/or fire starting pellets. Do NOT use** to start your fire:
   - Lighter fuel
   - Hair spray
   - Oil
   - WD-40

3. Once burning, add kindling:
   - Wood shavings
   - Dried shredded leaves
   - Pet bedding
   - Straw

4. Slowly add another handful of fuel; keep the bellows going to fan the flames. **Use your hive tool** to gently push the fuel to the bottom.
   - Small wood twigs
   - Wood chips

5. **Keep adding** small amounts of fuel and working the bellows. It can take 10 minutes or so to get the smoker full of burning fuel.

MORE STARTING A SMOKER TIPS

- **Do NOT fill a smoker full of fuel and set it on fire at the top.** A smoker works from the bottom up. Air is pushed through the smoker with the bellows at the bottom under the tray.

- **To test your smoke,** blow the smoke against your arm or the back of your knees. It should be cool to your skin.

- **If your smoke is too hot,** add dry leaves and allow to cool before using.

- **Swearing at your smoker will not help it start.** Take a deep breath; remove all contents; **try again.**

*Keep smoke a good 6 inches or more away from bees or you will burn their wings and antenna. **Smoke has to be cool!***

HOW TO USE A SMOKER

- **Smoke colony ahead of opening the hive.**

- **Keep a safe distance** so you are not alarming your bees.

- **Use smoke sparingly;** two to three puffs no less than 6" from bees.

- Smoke the entrance, then under the lid. **Wait** for the bees to pick up on the smoke, **about 30 seconds** to a minute.

- If working your colonies without gloves, **smoke your hands** without burning them. **Keep the smoker at a safe distance** when you do. It will take practice to know what that is.

- Keep smoker nose pointed in the **same direction as the wind.** If pointed in the opposite direction the smoke will not last as long or keep going as long.

- Smoke keeps your bees busy for about **10 minutes.**

- If working bees alone, set the lit smoker down with the **"business end" pointing in the direction, or downwind, of the breeze.** This creates a gradual, natural air flow through the fuel, keeping it smoldering.

- If you have a second person with you, **assign one person** to keep the smoker going. Someone will need to frequently work the bellows to keep the fire going and ensure it is not starting any unplanned fires.

CLOSING DOWN SMOKER

Close off the smoker spout, or chimney, with **a cork or thick stick.**

Put the flame out inside a **metal bucket or barrel.** Do not dump the hot contents on the ground or you may start a fire without realizing it. Those embers can smolder.

MUSLIN KITCHEN TOWELS

An alternative to using a smoker is to use **muslin kitchen towels, especially when colonies are small. It has to be muslin,** found in big box stores in kitchen section. Bees legs won't get caught in the muslin fabric as they may in terry towels.

Once the hive is open, **drape the kitchen towel** over the top of the hive. Fold it over in half; fold a second one over the other half. Move the fabric over as you remove frames.

When complete, remove the kitchen towels and close.

Muslin kitchen towels are **also handy when:**

- **Removing honey frames.** After removing bees, wrap the kitchen towel around the frame to protect it.
- Handy as neck scarves and head scarves **to collect beekeeper's sweat.**

*Drape **muslin kitchen towels over the hives to keep bees calm.** Often you can use muslin kitchen towels in lieu of a smoker.*

HOW MANY HIVE TOOLS DOES IT TAKE?

Buy at least two; you will inevitably misplace one when you need it most. Contrary to popular belief, planting hive tools in gardens will not grow new hive tools. (I wish!)

- **Start with one with a hook on one end;** that will make removing frames easier.
- **Small hive tools** are handy for those **quick peeks** you need to make under the lid.
- **Larger hive tools will give you more leverage** to unseal propolis and move the heavier hive bodies.
- **Paint or otherwise identify your hive tools.** They may get picked up by another beekeeper and get mistaken for their equipment. (Or deliberately misappropriated, although I am not naming names here. Yet.)
- Practice working your colonies with a **hive tool in one of your hands at all times**. Yes, it's a balancing act!
- **If you have a magnet, stick it in your back pocket.** That way you can easily attach the hive tool to the magnet when you are not using it. To remove, gently slip off magnet.
- **Periodically sharpen the end of your hive tools** so they will easily slip between the hive bodies.
- Don't pry open at box corners, you can easily destroy your hive boxes. **Apply the hive tool in the middle of the box** and gently push it downward. You should hear a small pop.
- **Always carry a hive tool when you are headed to your apiary.** If you want to get a few more daily steps in, leave it behind. You will be back to get it.

*Learn to work your **bees with a hive tool in hand.**
It takes a little practice but will be easier as you
get used to balancing the hive tool and frame.*

HOW MANY HIVE BOXES DO YOU NEED?

When starting, you can buy beginner packages that have the basic tools and a complete hive usually with a deep and two medium supers.

You will need at least **one extra super per colony** your first year. That extra super will be empty and will protect the supplemental food you may need to add inside the hive.

If nectar flows are strong, **your colony may also grow quickly.** Better to have an extra super or two than to be scrambling either borrowing or ordering more supers.

From bottom left moving clockwise: top hive feeder; Boardman feeder with glass jar; feeding shim with homemade ventilated inner cover; homemade escape board; two frame and one frame division board feeders; portable microscope; queen excluder; hive carrier.

OTHER BEEKEEPING ACCESSORIES

FEEDERS (*Do not open feed*)	NOTES
☐ **Boardman (Entrance) Feeders** use glass canning jars on elevated plastic platforms and metal lids with holes. Inexpensive. Designed for outside hive use but best used internally sitting on inner cover with an empty super around feeders, lid on top.	
☐ **Division Board Feeders** replace 1-2 inside frames and hold 1-2 gallons sugar syrup. Hive needs to be opened to refill.	
☐ **Top Hive Feeders** sit directly above brood nest. Bees crawl up the feeder from inside hive to get syrup. Holds 1-3 gallons depending on style. To refill, pull off lid, refill and close up colony.	
☐ **Feeding Shims** have wire bottoms bees can move through. They sit on top of frames under inner cover to provide supplemental sugar cakes and protein substitute. Also handy to provide a top hive entrance.	

BLOWERS	NOTES
☐ **Blowers** are used to remove bees off frames when extracting honey frames.	

ESCAPE BOARDS	NOTES
☐ **Escape Boards** are one-way traffic guides to remove bees from a hive prior to extracting honey frames.	

FUME BOARDS	NOTES

☐ **Fume Boards** are used with a bee detracting spray to quickly clear a honey super for easy removal.

INFARED THERMAL CAMERAS	NOTES

☐ **Infrared Thermal Cameras** are used in winter to check cluster location and other data depending on sensors and related applications.

MICROSCOPES	NOTES

☐ **Microscopes** are helpful for some pest and disease identification; they are also interesting to see bee and flower parts close up.

HIVE CARRIERS	NOTES

☐ **Hive carriers** are helpful to have if you plan on moving your hives from time to time. Requires two to use. Saves your back!

QUEEN EXCLUDERS	NOTES

☐ **Queen excluders** are metal or plastic grate worker bee size that prevents queen from moving between boxes.

CELL PHONE CAMERA	NOTES

☐ **Cell phones** are handy to have in the apiary for **narrating notes and taking photos/videos.** However, they can also easily get covered in propolis, honey and wax, not to mention fall out of a pocket. If you take your cell phone to your apiary, make sure you have it **tucked away** where it is safe.

MORE HANDY BEEKEEPING ACCESSORIES

Thumb tacks. To mark frames with queen cells or something else you are tracking. And **keep them in an old medicine container**. No fun sitting on them. Trust me.

*These are some of my **most-used beekeeping tools.** Some are available through beekeeping supply catalogs, others are makeshift.*

SAMPLE BASIC BEEKEEPING TOOLS AND EQUIPMENT

- **Notepad and pen** to take notes during hive checks and inspections;

- **Queen clip** to catch queen and place her in nucleus box for safekeeping;

- **Bee brush,** turkey feather that also works as a bee brush;

- **Smoker; long handled lighter or matches;**

- **Water bottle** for beekeeper to drink;

- **Alcohol** to clean beekeeping tools;

- Beekeeping **leather gloves;**

- **Muslin kitchen towels** to keep bees calm;

- **Nitrile (blue) gloves** to use in place of leather gloves to keep propolis off your hands and your beekeeping gloves. Bees can still sting through them so use if bees are calm.

- **Colored push pins** to mark frames for later checking;

- **Benadryl® pill** in case of stings;

- **Hive tool** before it's most likely misplaced in the apiary. I have mine painted blue for ease of identification.

- **Cell phone** (not visible) for photo and video taking. Be careful using your cell phone around your colonies, it can get propolis, honey and wax all over it.

FINDING A MENTOR

As you begin, **find a bee buddy,** someone who is starting at the same time you are. You can then exchange observations, visit each other's apiary and more quickly learn.

As you learn terminology and get some basics under your belt, look for an **experienced beekeeper close to where you live.** Ask if you can lend a hand at their apiary so you can observe. Follow up. As the relationship evolves, the two of you may find it to be a good opportunity to work together. You will be learning. The mentor will be getting an extra set of hands.

A mentor is NOT someone who is going to do the beekeeping for you.

Bungee Cords and Straps *will help keep your hives together. Bungee cords are good for securing lids. If you need to move a hive, use a strap so that nothing moves unless you move it.*

*Frame Rests. Make your own **frame rest** from a piece of wood cut to box size. Attach metal brackets to the wood so you can attach frame rest to the side of the hive. Add two long screws. The frame rest will hold one or two frames.*

*If you plan to mark your queens, a **one-handed queen catcher** is helpful. Use only beekeeping marking pens. Learn how to mark your queen by practicing on non-stinging drones.*

BEEKEEPING ETIQUETTE

This means different things in different areas. In general, **good beekeeping etiquette** covers several areas:

BE A GOOD NEIGHBOR

- If you have close neighbors, **talk to them** about your plans to have bees. Discuss how you plan to safeguard them from any issues.

- **Signage and fencing are must do's** to safely set up your apiary and protect your bees as well as your neighbors.

- If you, someone in your family and your neighbors plan to mow near and around the hives, make sure they are **properly dressed. Provide a bee suit on loan** just in case your bees take issue with the loud equipment sound. Don't mow so that grass clippings hit the hive entrance.

- During the holidays, **share your honey with neighbors.**

- If you are located close to a commercial beekeeping operation, realize **both of your apiaries** may impact the other one. Pay them a visit; work together.

- Some commercial operators have been known to give hobby beekeepers free queens to maintain the quality of the drone mating pool.

BE A CONSIDERATE FELLOW BEEKEEPER

- In the event you borrow equipment from another beekeeper, **return it in kind.** Thank them for the loan.

- **Be a bee buddy.** Find someone else at your equivalent level and share.

- When you can, **give back.** Help another beginning beekeeper.

- If you have other beekeepers close to where you live, introduce yourself and follow best management practices. Your bees will impact theirs and vice versa.

- If you are lucky enough to have a mentor, **be prepared and on time. Do your homework.**

- Don't try to keep bees by repeatedly texting your mentor. **Try to figure it out and your own research first.**

- **Thank your mentor** for taking the time to work with you.

- If you don't have a local bee club, **consider starting one.** Share information. Learn from each other.

THREE GENERAL BEEKEEPER CATEGORIES

The number of colonies may vary in each category. In general, these are the three beekeeper categories and the **range of colonies they have:**

- **Commercial:** depends on apiary for income. **(100+ hives)**
- **Sideliner:** partially gets income from beekeeping. **(41-100 hives)**
- **Hobbyist: (0-40 colonies)** Has all of the issues of the first two, none of the income, and **a lot more fun**. Yes, that's an editorial comment on my part. Ask any commercial beekeeper you know and see what he/she says.

Some beekeepers in the commercial and sideliner categories may get touchy when you ask them how many colonies they have. Since the number is tied to making money, **some don't want to share inside business information.**

Hobbyists, also called backyard beekeepers, on the other hand, tend to share their colony numbers **with pride and MUCH relished detail.**

GOOD TO KNOW

TIP

*If you would like to extract, bottle and sell honey, most states have licensing and annual inspection requirements. Municipal ordinances are concerned with public safety. State beekeeping laws and regulations are primarily designed to control diseases. Ultimately it's **the beekeeper's responsibility** to keep his/her colonies healthy.*

Your Notes

CHAPTER 5

About Honey Bees

HONEY BEE TYPES AND CHARACTERISTICS

The **Italian Honey Bee** has been the most utilized honey bee sub-species in North America.

Italians and Carniolan strains are usually recommended for beginning beekeepers because they are bred for gentleness, are easy on the new beekeepers and, when managed well, produce honey.

Through selective breeding, several other strains of honey bees with specific traits have been developed. Pure strains are maintained only when breeders have bee yards with only their own queen bees and drones.

Here are some of the **most common types and strains of bees** you may read and hear about.

*Sometimes bees can be **identified by their color.** Caramel-colored honey bees tend to be Italian Honey bees.*

HONEY BEE TYPES

"Ankle-Biters"	• Strain of bees developed in Indiana known for biting off *Varroa* mite legs. Also called Purdue Ankle Biters.
Buckfast	• Gentle, prolific queens • Good honey producers • Poor early spring pollinators
Carniolans or "Carnies"	• Early buildup and foraging • Good honey and pollen collecting • Usually winter well • Below average *Varroa* resistance
(Straight) Italians	• Good honey and pollen collection • Overwinter well • Low *Varroa* resistance
Minnesota Hygienic	• Gentle, good honey producers • American foulbrood/chalkbrood resistant • Highly prone to drifting • More likely to starve over winter
Russians	• Early building with good forage • Good honey producers • Overwinter well • Average *Varroa* resistance

"Saskatraz"	• Naturally resistant to *Varroa*, American foulbrood and chalkbrood. • Gentle, good honey producers. • Newest bee breed on market so still being tested and observed.
(Wild caught) Swarm	• Mixed/new genetics • Old queen/50% need to be requeened
VH1 (*Varroa* Sensitive Hygiene)	• Desired trait or behavior in some bee species • Remove *Varroa* mite-infested pupae • Leave pupae with non-reproductive mites
Feral	• Most wiped out in 2006-2007. Some remain in Arnot Forest and large forested areas.
Other:	

Notes:

_____

_____

_____

BASIC PARTS OF A WORKER BEE

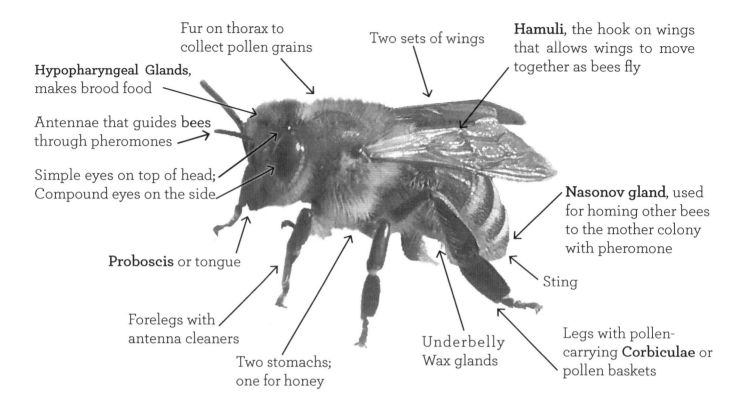

Fur on thorax to collect pollen grains

Two sets of wings

Hamuli, the hook on wings that allows wings to move together as bees fly

Hypopharyngeal Glands, makes brood food

Antennae that guides **bees** through pheromones

Simple eyes on top of head; Compound eyes on the side

Nasonov gland, used for homing other bees to the mother colony with pheromone

Proboscis or tongue

Sting

Forelegs with antenna cleaners

Two stomachs; one for honey

Underbelly Wax glands

Legs with pollen-carrying **Corbiculae** or pollen baskets

"BUSY AS A BEE"

The average **spring and summer worker bee lives for five to six weeks.** During this time, she'll produce around a twelfth of a teaspoon of honey during the average three weeks that she forages for food.

In winter, worker bees are morphologically different than spring or summer bees; they are designed to live longer. They **can live up to six months or more.** In addition to being honey bees raised for winter, they are also not wearing down their wings to keep the hive cool and dehydrating honey. They produce heat for the colony and tend to the Queen Bee.

HOW FAST DO HONEY BEES FLY?

· **Honey bees can fly up to 15-20 miles per hour** carrying nectar and pollen.

· They **move their shoulder muscles to produce the buzzing sound** of their wings: They move 200 times per second when hovering and 230 times per second in flight. By comparison, hummingbirds move their wings 102 times per second.

· **Per minute, honey bees move their wings 12,000 to 14,000 times.**

BUSY DANCERS

- Bees **communicate through dance** to share the resource locations.
- **The Round dance** is performed when the resource is located within 30 feet from the hive.
- The worker bee will enter the hive and **dance several circles, often reversing her direction** and pausing to share a taste of the resource she found.
- This dance indicates that bees can easily locate the resources by **flying in a circle around the hive** while searching for the floral odor present on the dancer.
- **The Sickle dance** is performed when the resource is located between 10 to 100 meters or 32 to 325 feet.
- The bee dances similar to the round dance except with **several crescent shaped formations** on the comb.
- **The Waggle dance** is performed when the resources is more than 100 meters or 325 feet away. It is different from the other two dances because it communicates **distance and direction.**
- The bee begins **vibrating (or waggling) as she walks in a precise direction, performing figure eights.** The time duration of the vibrating segment of the waggle dance is directly proportional to the distance the resource is located from the hive.
- The **direction of the vibrating segment is in relation to the position of the sun in the sky** used to determine the location of the nectar source in relation to the hive.

BEES KNEES

- The expression means **something or someone who is "cool"** and was popular in the US in the 1920s.
- **Corbiculae** are the hairs on worker bee legs where they pack and carry pollen back to the hive.

BEE GLUE

- Bees collect tree resin and mix it with honey, enzymes and other additives to make **propolis**, sometimes called "bee glue."

- In nature, bees **line their tree cavity homes** with propolis, ensuring a healthy environment for the colony.
- In a hive body, propolis will be found in hive body openings, in between frames and sealing down the inner cover.
- **Propolis looks like gooey caramel** and will stain bee gloves and your bee suit.
- It is **hard to remove.**
- **Work around it. Remove as little as possible**; propolis is keeping your colony healthy!

LAP OR SIP?

- **Honey bees lap up and sip** moisture, water, nectar and hummingbird syrup with their proboscis (tongue.) It can extend to ½ inch to reach nectar in bee friendly-designed flowers.
- **By contrast, butterflies and moths** use their straw-like proboscis to **sip water,** sugar and hummingbird syrup. That may explain why they tend to "sit" or light on flowers when they are feeding.

BEE BREATH

Honey bees breathe through a set of **spiracles, or holes in their thorax, similar to a dolphin's blowhole.** They can hold their breath for only short periods of time. That's why they head back to the hive when rain is imminent.

MAKING WAX

Worker bees have 4 pairs of **wax glands** under their abdomen. These glands produce small, flat wax "scales." Worker bees move the scale with the pollen basket spines to their front legs. They then mix in saliva as she chews the wax scale. The wax scale is stacked to form wax comb. Burr comb is comb drawn in unwanted spaces.

MAKING BABY FOOD

Worker bees also consume beebread to activate their hypopharyngeal glands, or *food glands* so they secrete *royal jelly,* a milky-white protein rich food fed to all larvae in their first 3 days of life.

*Honey bees have **cushy foot pads** that allow them to stand on grass, car windshields and a bee suit. Or two.*

Life Cycle of Honey Bees

Honey bees are Eusocial and have different jobs (age polytheism) moving from job to job (temporal polytheism) depending on age. They also have two castes, or designated jobs; fertile queens and non-sexually mature worker bees. Drones do not work.

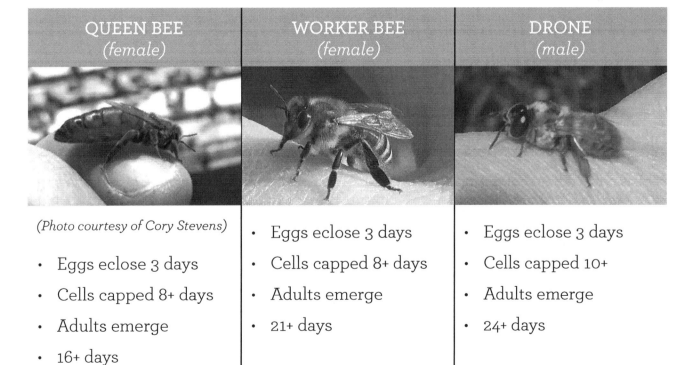

QUEEN BEE *(female)*	WORKER BEE *(female)*	DRONE *(male)*
(Photo courtesy of Cory Stevens)		
• Eggs eclose 3 days	• Eggs eclose 3 days	• Eggs eclose 3 days
• Cells capped 8+ days	• Cells capped 8+ days	• Cells capped 10+
• Adults emerge	• Adults emerge	• Adults emerge
• 16+ days	• 21+ days	• 24+ days

QUEEN BEE LIFE (one per colony)	SPRING & SUMMER WORKER BEES LIVES (85-90% of a colony)	THE LIFE OF A DRONE (10-15% of colony)

- Queens carry **50% of the colony's genetics.**

- The Queen Bee is the **largest bee in the colony.**

- **The Queen Bee's** wings only make **it halfway down her abdomen.** She also has the **largest thorax** and long pointy behind.

- Queens are **exclusively fed royal jelly.**

- She is often surrounded by her **"retinue" or attendants.**

- **Virgin queens are smaller** and don't have a pheromone.

- A well-mated queen will mate with **15-20 drones.**

- Once mated, **it can take a few days** before the queen starts to lay.

- Each mated queen bee has a unique pheromone or scent worker bees recognize.

- **Worker bees** have pointed bottoms and wings covering their abdomens.

- Young worker bees have **fur on their thorax.**

- Day old eggs will **stand straight up.**

WORKER BEE JOBS

- 1-3 days hardening body/learning to fly.

- 2-4 days House bee; cell cleaning

- 4-11 Nurse bee feeding larvae. Mortuary bee removing bodies.

- 7-12 Queen retinue.

- 12-16 Hive fanning.

- 12-18 Water carrying; nectar transfer.

- 18-20 Hive guarding.

- 12-35 Honeycomb building and honey sealing

- 12-42 Foraging; collect nectar, pollen, propolis

- Drones carry **50% of the colony's genetics.**

- Drone pupae eyes are big enough to touch each other.

- Drones are **often mistaken for queen bee** because they are larger than worker bees.

- A drone develops from an unfertilized egg.

- They **don't have a sting.**

- **Worker bees initially feed drones** eclosing; then drones feed themselves.

- Drones have **short tongues** so they can't collect nectar.

- **Drones do not do any work inside the hive** although reports they sit around playing games and watching TV are highly exaggerated. (Not disproven yet but still...)

QUEEN BEE LIFE (one per colony)	WORKER BEE JOBS	THE LIFE OF A DRONE (10-15% of colony)
• A mated queen bee lives **most of her life** inside the hive. • Worker bees **slim down a queen** prior to swarming so she can fly with the swarm. • If the older queen is injured or can't fly, the colony will leave the old queen with the original colony and the daughter will lead the swarm. • If the queen bee is marked, the queen bee thorax has a **dab of special paint** usually color coordinated to the year. The mark makes it easier to spot the queen. • Queen bee mandibles are toothed with an end cusp and are used to dig her way out of queen cell. • A well-mated queen will lay some 1,500 eggs a day during the spring build up and store the sperm she will use for the rest of her reproductive life.	• **Workers may revert to earlier or later duties as needed.** • Worker bees may be a **range of different color combinations** in the same colony. • All bees smell through **their antennae and their feet.** Workers produce odors used for alarm and colony defense. Worker bees sting when the threat object is moving. • Worker bees have unique mandibles to mould wax, collect propolis, move dead bodies and debris. They also bite *Varroa* mites. **WINTER WORKER BEES** • Born August. **Live from fall until early spring.** • Keep only cluster warm (not hive) by shivering flight muscles. • Winter worker bees consume honey located over the cluster; that is the warmest hive spot besides the cluster.	• Their **main function is to mate** with virgin or newly mated queens. • Drones find **"drone congregation areas"** to mate and re-use them year to year. • Drones have large eyes to **better spot queen while flying.** • **Drone antennae** are designed to detect queen pheromone. • The drone was supposedly named after the **droning noise** it makes beating its wings. • A drone only has a grandfather; no father. • **Drone** mandibles are similar to **queen bee** mandibles and cusped at the bottom. They are used to escape from their cells. • Drones and **queen bees** lack the feeding grove in worker bee mandibles so they don't help raise brood.

And now it's time for a fun test, let's see...

What Do You Know! POP QUIZ

*This is a **typical medium frame of brood** from one of my colonies. It has drones, worker bees and a lovely Italian queen bee.*

Can you spot the three different bees on this frame? Where are they? What characteristics did you notice that helped you spot them?

Your Answer:

_____

Worker bees are eusocial, multigenerations of bees supporting a laying queen and working as one as a "superorganism."

MORE ABOUT HONEY BEE LIFE CYCLE

LONG LIVE THE QUEEN	QUITE THE DANCERS	GOOD GUYS, REALLY
• The queen bee is busiest in spring/summer when she can **lay 1,200-2,000 eggs a day,** the equivalent to her own body weight.	• Worker bees **communicate through dance** to indicate food source locations.	• Drones **mate only** during flight.
• **A swarming queen will leave a newly-eclosed daughter behind** to lay for the mother colony.	• The sound a honey bee makes is from moving shoulder muscles to beat wings 11,400 times per minute.	• They are paralyzed during mating, **then die after they mate when their abdomen is ripped open.**
• If the old queen is damaged, **the daughter will leave** with the swarm.	• **Worker bees beat their wings 200 times per second** hovering and 230 times a second in flight.	• Queen may return to hive with a "mating sign," the drone's endophallus bulb in her sting chamber. Worker bees remove it.
• **A queen bee has a sting.**	• Worker bees move their wings more than twice the rate of hummingbirds.	• Drones that survive mating flights are ejected from hive.
• A queen bee tends to use her **sting only on other eclosing or emerging queens** to kill them.	• Honey bees have 170 odorant receptors in their antenna and fewer taste buds.	• **Drone cells look like pencil erasers and are larger than worker cells.**
• **In nature,** a queen bee may **live 4-5 years.**	• **Worker bees use color, shapes, pheromones and electrical charges** to locate flowers and to navigate back to their original home.	• Worker bees toss drones out during periods of dearth and preparing for winter. **Drones do not overwinter with the rest of the colony.**
• In managed colonies, **queen bees may be replaced 1-2 years.**		• The colony will grow new drones next spring.
• **Supercedure cells are queen cells built to replace aging and no longer functioning queens.**		• Drones can **visit other colonies** without being challenged by guard bees.

- Swarm cells are **daughter queens** raised to stay with the colony when the old queen leaves with a swarm.

- Worker bees **recognize the face** of their beekeeper.
- Worker bees may recycle wax.

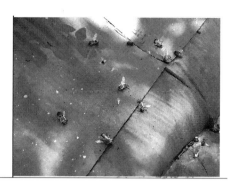

HOW TO READ A BROOD FRAME

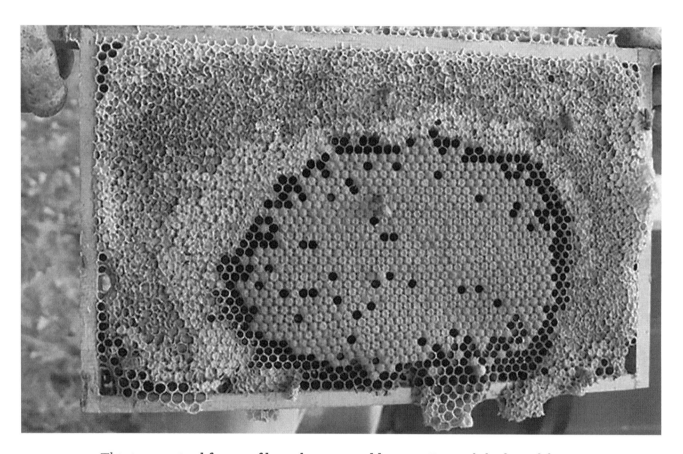

*This is **a typical frame of brood or capped larvae.** Around the brood frame center you want to see beebread, or different-colored pollen mixed with bee saliva and covered with a thin honey layer. The honey rainbow band around the beebread is another readily available food source. Nurse bees need beebread to activate their hypopharyngeal or food glands to secrete royal jelly to feed to all larvae up to three days old and to queens during their whole lives. Healthy 3 or 4 day old larvae appear pearly white.*

You can start to assess how well a colony is doing by understanding what you are observing on a frame of brood. The frames with eggs are called **brood frames.** Brood frames tend to be located in the bottom center of 1 to 2 hive boxes. That is considered the **brood nest.**

All bees start as an egg. The queen bee lays an egg in the wax cell bottom. The eggs are usually laid in an oval shape design in the middle to bottom of a frame.

The eggs develop in three days. During those 3 days, all eggs are fed "bee milk" or "royal jelly." **Royal jelly** is a white milky substance, a combination of water, proteins and sugars, produced by glands on nurse bees heads. Nurse bees are young worker bees that have yet to leave the hive.

If you can't see your queen, look for the tiny rice-like shape in the royal jelly. That means that your **queen bee has been laying in the last 3 days.** Spotty brood patterns can be caused by pests and diseases and do not always mean a failing queen.

When assessing your colony's strength, you will be doing so **based on the number of brood frames.** You will want at least 6 frames of brood prior to a nectar flow; that will ensure that you have a good number of foraging worker bees to collect nectar and pollen. Larger colonies collect more nectar than smaller ones.

If you want to split one colony into two, you will need at least 3 brood frames to remain with the original colony and at least another 2 brood frames, honey and beebread to place into a nuc.

To assess **when new bees will emerge** from brood frames to estimate colony size:
- Worker bee larvae are fed a mix of fermented pollen and honey, then get sealed and become pupae that emerge as fully functioning female **worker bees** in **21 days.** Newly emerging worker bees will access nearby stored beebread and capped honey.
- If the larva is **a drone,** it will be fed a mix of fermented pollen and honey until sealed. Drones emerge in **24 days.**
- Queen bee larvae will exclusively be fed royal jelly until sealed with a wax cap. The queen emerges in **15-18 days.**

KNOW YOUR QUEEN CELLS

*Worker bees build three queen bee cell types: **supercedure, swarm and emergency.** Worker bees are basically replacing the current queen. Supercedure cells tend to be built into comb, frame center. Swarm cells look like **peanuts usually hanging off frame sides and bottoms.** Once swarm cells are sealed, **the colony may swarm at any time.***

Worker bees will build **emergency queen cups** that look like small round wax cups on the side of frames. If you see a white milky substance inside, the bees are using that emergency queen cup to raise a new queen. If not, remove these emergency queen cups before introducing a new queen. Otherwise leave them on the frame.

Workers bees may also build **supercedure** and **swarm cells.** Those queen cells look like a peanut. Supercedure queen cells are built on comb to raise a new queen to replace the existing one. The existing queen may be injured or has stopped laying.

Swarm cells are also peanut-looking cells that tend to be built on the frame bottom. Once queen swarm cells are capped, the colony may swarm.

CHECKING FOR SWARM CELLS

To **quickly check for swarm cells** in the spring, open and raise the brood box so you can look underneath the frames. Check to see if you can spot swarm cells on frame bottoms.

When temperatures are 70°F+, more closely inspect the colony for queen cells by going through the frames.

During the nectar flow, check colonies every 7-10 days for possible new queen cells.

If you spot queen swarm cells, you can move those cells to a nuc to start a new colony and to a queenless colony. Do not leave the swarm cells in the hive or you may lose the whole colony to swarming.

*To **quickly check for queen swarm cells,** lift the super and look at the bottom of the frames. Queen swarm cells tend to be built on or towards frame bottoms. If you see swarm cells, then make a decision about what to do with them by either removing into nucs to start a new colony or placing in another queenless colony.*

WHAT HONEY BEES EAT

Honey bee food determines their **overall health. Good nutrition from excellent foraging sources** during the growing season **is a must** for the honey bees' good health.

- **The best bee food is the honey they make!**
- **Do not feed honey bees store purchased honey.** You could be introducing diseases and contaminating your colonies.
- Sometimes beekeepers will feed their off-putting honey, such as honey that smells like dirty socks from native goldenrod, back to their colonies in an **emergency.**
- Plants produce nectar and pollen with **a range of amino acids, vitamins and minerals** depending on the plant and growing conditions.

Bees collect nectar for flight fuel; they dehydrate nectar to 16-18% converting flower nectar to stored honey primarily for winter consumption. Spring honey is light; fall honey is dark. Bees will also eat their stored honey during the late summer dearth.

*Bees gather pollen and store it mixed with honey and water as **beebread**. Nurse bees consume the bee bread to produce food with their hypopharyngeal glands. Beebread will be different color depending on the type of pollen included.*

HONEY BEE FOOD SOURCES	
FOOD	PURPOSE
Honey	**Main carbohydrate source** to feed growing larvae; to feed bees during winter and as flight fuel.
Beebread	**Flower pollen mixed with honey, nectar and bee saliva,** which contains enzymes and beneficial microbes. Packed pollen is sealed with a thin honey film. Nurse bees consume beebread to activate their food glands to produce baby food i.e., royal jelly.
Royal Jelly	**Protein-rich secretion from worker bee food glands.** All larvae are fed royal jelly in the first 3 days; queens are fed royal jelly during their larval stage and throughout their adult lives.
Pollen	Main protein source from **reproducing plants.** Pollen is stored as beebread. Nurse bees consume pollen to activate food glands to produce royal jelly. A good variety of pollen ensures all of the vitamins, minerals and amino acids needed to keep colony healthy.

Nectar	**Plant secretion to entice pollinators,** nectar is flight fuel and is stored, then dehydrated, for winter food, called honey.
Water	Needed for digestion, waste removal and to liquefy granulated honey and sugar. Water also helps to cool and humidify the hive. Critical to honeybee nutrition; bees can't live for more than a few days without it. **Bees prefer water with minerals, enzymes and amino acids. In other words, "dirty water."**
Microbial Meat *(That's right, bees are not vegan, they are omnivores)*	**Beneficial bacteria and fungi naturally occurring in pollen.** Bees need these non-plant proteins to complete their growth and development. They increase pollen's nutritional value by adding amino acids, protein's building blocks, that flowering plants alone may not always provide.
Cracked Corn	Bees **may visit bird feeders** and pick up pollen associated with cracked corn in the bird feed mix.
Hummingbird Sugar Water	**Honey bees will turn to hummingbird feeders** when they can't find nectar in nature, usually at the start of the late summer dearth, when plants are not producing nectar and pollen.
Dung and Fruit	Honey bees will collect **vitamins, minerals, amino acids** they need from whatever sources they can find. ***Depending on other available food sources,** bees may visit bananas, pears, and watermelon, sometimes rotting.

HOW BEST TO FEED HONEY BEES

The best way to feed your honey bees is to **provide them a wide range of pollen and nectar sources**—that means a lot of plants in nature—during the growing season.

Over winter, the best way to feed your bees is to **leave them enough honey** on their own combs and frames to feed themselves until Spring.

HOW TO TEMPORARILY SUPPLEMENT FEED HONEY BEES

If, however, honey bees don't have enough food, here are some **temporary feeding options** and why.

This is NOT a substitute for real plant food! Remember that some winter losses are natural and expected.

Supplemental sugar cakes provided a colony during winter in a top feeding shim in addition to extra honey. The sugar cakes also help to absorb moisture.

SUPPLEMENTAL BEE FEEDING

NECTAR SUBSTITUTE

In general, supplement feed if:

- you have **caught a swarm;**
- are **installing a package;**
- **getting a nuc;**
- **making a split,** especially if later in the season, such as June and beyond, and
- if your bees **are struggling** because of lack of food.

SUPPLEMENTAL SUGAR SYRUP FEEDING

Sugar syrup, or sugar feeding, temporarily provides bees with carbohydrates, which is energy.

Man-made sugar syrup does not contain the vitamins, minerals and amino acids available in nature.

HOW TO MAKE SUGAR SYRUP

1. Heat water. Water does not need to boil.
2. Add sugar and stir until dissolved. **Do not cook your sugar.** Let cool.
3. Add lemongrass in spring but not summer or fall to reduce robbing. **Feed inside your hives.**
4. **Keep in refrigerator** when not in use.
5. **When making a gallon or more at a time,** a paint mixer on a cordless drill can make short work of the task, especially in the mixing of the heavier 2:1 syrup. Keep reading, the sugar to water ratios vary; explanation coming up!

HOW TO FEED SUGAR SYRUP

Feed sugar syrup inside the hive; **do not open feed.**

There are several types of feeders. **The easiest way for beginning beekeepers to feed sugar syrup** is to use Boardman feeders inside the hive:

- **Boardman feeders** keep the lid elevated so bees can reach the sugar syrup; you can also use two small sticks placed under the overturned lid with holes attached to a glass jar covered with an empty super.

- To install a jar of sugar syrup, **first turn the glass jar over** and let the natural seal stop the sugar syrup from dripping. Best not to shower bees in sugar syrup, it can drown them.

- **Replace every couple of days** in hot temperatures.

- **Do not** feed sugar syrup **in winter**; the syrup will freeze.

BASICS OF SUGAR SYRUP FEEDING

(first number sugar, second water)

- Do not perpetually feed, this is just to give your bees a little help.

WHY SPRING FEED

1:1 light syrup (by weight, 8 pounds sugar to 1 gallon water)

- Sugar syrup resembles the wide range of plant nectars **without the vitamins, minerals and amino acids** plants provide.

- **This is NOT the same thing** as plant nectar or honey!

- Studies show **bees cannot live** on sugar syrup alone.

SO WHY FEED SUGAR SYRUP?

- To **stimulate wax glands** so worker bees draw out wax foundation, especially plastic foundation.

- To **simulate nectar flow** and speed up egg laying.

- To **supplement short honey stores** so bees don't starve.

WHEN BEST TO FEED SUGAR SYRUP

- **Feed six weeks before the nectar flow** to ensure higher bee population.

- **Do not overfeed.** Too much will result in sugar syrup bound brood area, which means there will be **no room for queen to lay** and may lead to **early swarming.**

- Good reason to **check frames** to make sure queen bee has room to lay.

WHY FALL FEED?

2:1 heavy syrup (sugar to water)

- To **fill up cells** so there's no brood going into winter.

- To **provide winter stores** for late-starting colonies.

*Use Boardman feeders inside hives by adding an empty super to protect feeder. **Don't open feed**, that spreads **Varroa** and encourages robbing. In photo, two Boardman feeders providing supplemental sugar syrup and recommended size of supplemental pollen patties, as needed, during spring and summer.*

SUGAR CAKES, CANDY BOARDS, MOUNTAIN CAMP

The following are **three easy ways** to provide supplemental sugar, from making winter sugar cakes in advance to emergency feeding.

SUGAR CAKES RECIPE

- Provides **supplemental food** at the end of the winter season
- Helps **absorb hive moisture** during winter

Ingredients

- *5 pounds or 11¼ cups sugar*
- *1 teaspoon *white distilled vinegar*
- **don't use apple cider vinegar, it attracts small hive beetles*
- *1 teaspoon bee healthy essential oil mixture*
- *7½ ounces of water, measured exactly*

* For January-February early Spring feeding, add ¼ cup protein substitute to sugar for each batch.

1. Add bee healthy and vinegar to measuring cup; add water to make 7½ ounces. Mix well.
2. Spread in bread pans, repurposed fruit clam shells, pie pans. One batch fills six rectangular fruit clam shells.
3. Leave overnight in cold oven to dry out. Once top is dry, **remove from container** and turn over on a cookie sheet to let bottom dry out for a couple of days.
4. If **still moist, remix** and add more sugar; dry again.
5. Store **in sealed plastic container** until needed.

*If sugar cakes become dry and brittle in feeding shim, spray with water to soften sugar mixture so bees can get to it.

*No need to add lemongrass oil. Lemongrass oil attracts bees to the top when they should be in the cluster.

BASIC CANDY BOARD RECIPE

Candy boards are good options for providing **additional food through winter.** You can buy candy boards or make your own with a feeding shim.

Candy Board dimensions: 20" long, 16¼ inches wide, 2½ inches tall.

Ingredients

- *1 tablespoon white vinegar*
- *16 pounds sugar*
- *3 cups water per batch*

1. Pour 1 tablespoon of vinegar into 3 cups of water.
2. Add 8 pounds of sugar in a large mixing bowl. Slowly add 1½ cups of water/vinegar mixture while stirring with a large spoon. **Consistency should be of wet sand.**
3. Dump sugar into the candy board. **Evenly pack down the sugar.** Leave a space around the entrance hole by placing a block of wood in front of the hole. Pack sugar around it.
4. Pour the remaining 8 pounds of sugar into mixing bowl. Add remaining 1½ cups of water/vinegar to the sugar while stirring with a large spoon. Add the remaining sugar to the candy board. **Pack it in tight.**
5. **Wait 24 hours** for the candy board to fully dry. Add to your hives.

*Candy boards can be **homemade or purchased;** this one was purchased in 2011 and was still viable 10 years later. Beekeeper forgot he had it!*

MOUNTAIN CAMP EMERGENCY WINTER FEEDING

"Mountain Camp" was a Beesource.com **message board user name.** The user explained how he simply fed his bees sugar in winter. The concept is based on the idea that when you are camping, you tend to rely on simpler methods of getting things done.

In some circles, this is considered **a last resort** way to winter feed. **It should not be used as your first option.**

Ingredients

- *1-2 pages of newspaper*
- *4 pounds sugar*
- *Spray bottle*
- *Feeding shim (optional)*

1. If you have a feeding shim or extra hive body, **place above top frames**.
2. Place 1 page of newspaper over top frames leaving one inch around the edges; **spray newspaper with water.**
3. Pour sugar to 1" thickness; **spray sugar.**
4. **Add more sugar** spread out over newspaper ensuring the sugar is wet.
5. The heat of the hive will basically keep sugar easy to access.
6. If the sugar dries out, **spray again with water.** Bees will remove dry sugar from the hive.
7. If you find dry sugar in the bottom box, that's an indication the **bees couldn't access it** for supplemental food because it was too dry.

*In the mountain camp emergency feeding, remember to **add a space rim or empty super** to give bees room to safely access the sugar.*

SUPPLEMENTAL BEE FEEDING POLLEN SUBSTITUTE

In nature, pollen is how plants reproduce. Pollen is the equivalent of male plant cells. Bees move pollen from the anther of one flower to the stigma of another flower, making it possible for plants to generate seeds and reproduce.

One of my favorite past times is to **watch my bees bringing in the different pollen colors.** Some days its hard to miss those large yellow pollen-packed legs as they crash land at the entrance.

Some beekeepers **trap pollen in times of plenty to freeze** and feed back to the bees later. Studies show frozen pollen is more beneficial for the bees than commercial pollen substitutes or dried pollen.

SMALL HIVE BEETLE FOOD

When overused, pollen substitute patties are excellent unintended small hive beetle food. Small hive beetles will lay eggs in the patties.

Feed honey bees small quantities (1-2 inch squares). Periodically check that small hive beetle larvae aren't hatching underneath.

Remove any pollen substitutes not being utilized by the bees.

WHEN TO FEED POLLEN SUBSTITUTE

Yep, you see it coming, don't you. **"It depends!"**

Some areas prominently monoculture, such as corn and soybean fields, **may need pollen supplements** to give honey bees a variety of pollen. Not all pollen is alike.

In other cases, the need to supplement feed pollen can be driven by weather. Colonies caught in late spring rains that can't forage **may need pollen supplements to keep growing brood fed.**

In general, **feed pollen substitute** when your bees are growing the colony:
- Mid-February **when temperatures are 50°F or more.**
- **Build up** to Spring nectar flow.
- When **colony is struggling** and needs to build up.

- **Do not feed pollen substitute in the open.**
- **In most cases, do not feed pollen substitute late in the season.** Queen should be laying less eggs and bees should have enough beebread stored. The operative word here is "should."

If you need, or choose to feed pollen during winter, **select a pollen substitute that is mostly carbohydrates.** Bees aren't raising much brood in winter so, in theory, they don't need ready access to pollen.

HOMEMADE PROTEIN PATTIES RECIPE
(Small Amount)

Ingredients

- *1 cup protein substitute*
- *3 cups sugar*
- *1 cup honey*
- *1 cup shortening*
- *1 flat tablespoon brewer's yeast*
- *1 teaspoon salt*

1. **Mix with hands**; makes a thick heavy paste.
2. Use a golf ball size amount **flattened to ¼ inch** thickness, cut in half.
3. **Place directly over brood** to give nurse bees access to protein they can use to produce brood food.

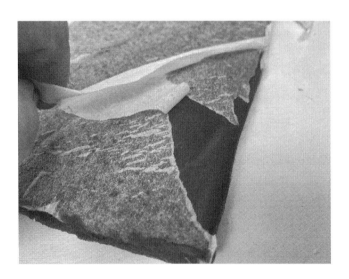

*If you have wax paper on protein patties, **no need to remove,** the bees will do that once it is inside the hive.*

HOMEMADE PROTEIN PATTIES RECIPE

(Large Amount)

Ingredients

- *25 lbs. sugar*
- *2 quarts white vinegar*
- *2 quarts cold water*
- *1½ cups vegetable oil*
- *½ teaspoon electrolytes*
- *1 teaspoon citric or ascorbic acid*
- *7 lbs Brewer's yeast*
- *7 lbs protein substitute*

1. Mix **first six ingredients** well in a 5-gallon bucket with large paint paddle and drill to easily combine.

2. **Add a little at a time** in equal parts 7 lbs Brewer's yeast and 7 lbs protein substitute.

3. Mixture will be soft; **let it sit overnight to thicken.** You want it soft but not runny. It should sit on top of frames without oozing through.

4. **Store in airtight container.**

DO NOT OPEN FEED

*Store unused protein patties in a dry cool place or they **will become breeding grounds** for lesser wax moths.*

ESSENTIAL OIL FEEDING STIMULANT RECIPE

This **general purpose essential oil mixture** is a feeding stimulant. It is similar to other commercially available bee healthy products.

Ingredients

- *5 cups sugar or 2.5 lbs sugar*
- *4 cups water*
- *⅛ teaspoon lecithin granules*
- *15 drops food grade lemongrass oil*
- *15 drops food grade spearmint oil*

1. Bring water to boil; **stir in sugar until dissolved**. Remove mixture from heat and quickly add lecithin and essential oils.

2. **Stir mixture thoroughly.** Don't add essential oils while sugar mixture is on stove; heat weakens them.

3. **Cool before using.**

4. **Store in refrigerator.**

5. **Shake** prior to using.

Solutions should have **a strong scent** and **NOT be left** in the open around bees. A little goes a long way!

HOW TO USE ESSENTIAL OIL FEEDING STIMULANT

1. **Two teaspoons in a quart of 1:1 sugar/water syrup or 1 teaspoon to one cup of 1:1 sugar water.**

   - **Helps rapid buildup** when used as a feeding stimulant.
   - Use in **early spring** to **build up packages, nucs and swarms** and during periods when no **nectar** is available.

2. Four teaspoons in a quart of 1:1 sugar/water syrup:

- Spray bees to **calm them** instead of smoke.
- Dab on **queen thorax** to help with new queen introduction.
- **Dab on your hand** to minimize stings.
- Lightly **spray on bees** to prevent fighting when combining nucs, swarms and colonies.
- Spray lightly on package bees to keep them calm.
- **Spray on new foundation** to encourage bees to draw out new and plastic comb.

Helpful to Know for the Tired Beekeeper

According to Dr. Kirsten Traynor in *Two Million Blooms, Discovering the Medicinal Benefits of Honey*, honey can prevent fatigue.

CITRUS HONEY THIRST QUENCHER

(For fatigue in place of sports drinks)

Ingredients

- *½ cup honey*
- *¼ cup fresh-squeezed lemon or lime juice*
- *7½ cups water*

1. *Mix ingredients in large pitcher. **Slightly warm water** will help dissolve the honey.*
2. ***Chill** if desired.*

GOOD TO KNOW
TIP

*Bees will **raid hummingbird feeders** when they are hungry. Use ⅛th inch screen over the feeder holes. Bees can't access the sugar water but hummingbirds can.*

Your Notes

Your Notes

_____

_____

_____

_____

_____

_____

_____

_____

_____

CHAPTER 6
How to Get Honey Bees

GET BEES WHEN THEY HAVE THE MOST TIME TO GROW

Once you know you have the right conditions to successfully host honey bees, then it's time to discuss how to get them. This is mostly **about timing.** You want to get bees at the **beginning of your growing season** so they have time, and available resources, to settle in. Beginning colonies will need time to expand so they have enough bees to collect pollen to feed newly emerging bees and flower nectar they dehydrate into honey for winter food.

If they are not already established, either in a nuc or standard hive, the colony may spend their initial year building comb. Hopefully they will also have enough time and bees to make honey for themselves. Depending on available resources, it can take on the **average 1-3 years** before a colony produces **extra honey to share with the beekeeper.**

In other words, if you want to get a jump start on keeping bees, get established colonies such as nucs. The small colony already has a laying mated queen and bees are ready for more space to expand.

*Buying nucleus (nucs) colonies, right, is **one of the ways beginning beekeepers get starter bee colonies.** Healthy nucs can be jam packed full of bees so have your full hives on hand and ready to transfer your colonies soon after getting them. My bee buddies David, left and Tom, right, helping a new beekeeping student set up a first hive.*

You are also ordering your bees **months ahead** of when they will be delivered, usually the fall before the spring. That gives beekeepers providing and selling bees enough time to get their needed supplies and bees themselves.

The following are options for getting bees with advantages, disadvantages, and estimated costs:

HOW TO GET HONEY BEES

(Check all you are considering)			
METHOD	COST	PROS	CONS
☐ Package Bees	$100-$150	Most available; lower cost; one way to select bee breed.	50% failure or supersedure in the first couple of months, may require new queen. Need to feed to pull wax. Challenging to install for new beekeepers.
☐ Nuc (Nucleus Colony)	$150+	Established small colony; laying Queen; easy to transfer to larger hive.	Weather dependent; picking up nuc from supplier may be delayed due to weather issues.
☐ Established Colony	$300+	Established bee colony; proven over-wintered genetics.	Transportation; Possibly importing diseases; Equipment may need to be replaced.

☐ Catch Swarms	$50+ Cost of trap, lures	Bees are looking for a home; survivor genetics.	Your availability. Bee location can be challenging to reach. Swarm may not stay once housed.
☐ Split Existing Colony	$300+ Possible cost for Queen, cost for new woodenware.	Easy to perform, prevents swarming.	Timing. Location of new colony.
☐ Being Given an Existing Colony and Hive	Possible cost for Queen, cost for new woodenware.	No expense to purchase colony.	Status of *Varroa* mite management and managing for *Varroa* and other diseases.

Notes:

_____

_____

_____

PACKAGE BEES OR NUCS?

PACKAGE BEES	
ADVANTAGES	**CHALLENGES**
• Slow "build up," allowing beginning beekeepers time to get used to handling bees and working a colony. • May **already be treated** for *Varroa* mites. (Ask when ordering)	• Worker bees are not bonded to the included queen; the queen may leave, requiring re-queening. • Colony may decide to requeen. • Colony may leave.

NUCLEUS OR NUCS	
ADVANTAGES	**CHALLENGES**
• Queen is already established and laying. • Rapid bee population growth.	• If increasing hive space requirements are not managed and met, may swarm.

*Place package bees **gently inside hive** to install colony.*

HOW TO INSTALL PACKAGE BEES

Order your honey bees as soon as you can. Most suppliers start taking orders late Fall and are sold out by early Spring.

Some suppliers may come up short once it's time to deliver bees so have a backup source identified, just in case.

Set up your hive in its permanent location with

- a hive stand
- bottom board
- entrance reducer
- brood box with frames and foundation
- empty medium super
- inner cover
- top cover and
- feeder

In addition, **make 1:1 sugar syrup** in a spray bottle for the time you are settling bees in.

Once you pick up/receive package bees:

- **Inspect for health of bees.** Some few dead bees are normal.
- Check that **queen in her cage is still alive.**
- **Check can of syrup** to determine if bees may be hungry.

Remove half of the frames in the brood box. Spray 1:1 sugar syrup over half of the frames, removing each as you spray them.

Add package into the open space in brood box. Do NOT shake bees into the box, you will kill more bees by doing so. Be gentle and patient.

Remove the syrup can and remove the queen in her cage.

- If queen cage has sugar plug, leave as is.
- If queen cage only has a cork, **add a sugar plug** by mixing honey with confectioner's sugar until you have a thick paste. Gently remove cork and add the sugar plug in its place.
- Leave cork off; bees will eat their way through sugar and release themselves, and the queen bee, from the queen cage.

Hang the queen cage in between frames with the **screen area accessible** to worker bees. Make sure the screen area is not against the frames.

Add a sugar syrup feeder over the existing frames.

*Package of bees **settled inside** their new hive home.*

Add the medium super, inner cover and top cover.

Close the entrance reducer **to the smallest size.**

In a couple of days, check the package. Most if not all bees should be out.
- Remove the package; lean it against the hive so remaining bees can leave.
- Check queen in cage.
- Replace frames in void left after removing package.

By about the fourth day, queen should be released from queen cage. If not, check daily to make sure she is still alive, being fed and cared for by worker bees.

Once queen is released, **leave them alone for 10-14 days.**

If queen has been accepted, easily recognized capped brood will start appearing. If not, the package supplier should be contacted for instructions.

Once a new queen has been successfully introduced, continue to **feed the colony** to help them build up numbers.

Packages in Midwest are usually delivered April-June time frame, almost the middle to the end of the spring nectar flow.

A package colony will need to be fed **during its first year** to build up enough colony numbers to make it through winter. The build-up includes constructing comb, which takes a lot of energy. It takes bees eight times the energy to make a pound of comb as it does to produce a pound of honey.

SHAKING PACKAGES

You've seen the videos of beekeepers shaking packages into a hive. I don't recommend that as you begin. Beginning beekeepers have a **tendency to shake too hard** and kill bees.

If for whatever reason you can't wait for bees to move into a hive:

- Remove the sugar syrup can
- Remove the queen in her queen cage
- Remove half the frames in the hive

Turn package over and gently—**GENTLY**—shake bees into the open hive area. **Do NOT smack** the package against the hive; you will kill bees doing that.

Wait a minute or so. Once again gently shake bees into the open hive area.

- Add frames back in.
- Hang the queen cage in between frames with the screen area accessible to worker bees.
- When most of the bees are in hive, place the package at the front of the hive.
- Give colony sugar water inside the hive.

WHEN TO ADD A SUPER

Once your bees have the wax drawn on all inside frames and are working the **two outside frames of the brood box**, it is time to add more room.

You don't want to provide too much space or small hive beetles will remain unchecked. If you **crowd the bees,** they may be **tempted to swarm.**

As you add supers, **you need to check the initial hive box** to make sure the **queen still has room to lay.** If not, you move honey frames from the bottom box to the new next box and provide new frames for the bees to draw comb. You can also add frames with drawn comb.

LAYING WORKER BEES

When a colony loses a queen, **it takes 2-3 weeks** for the queen pheromone to dissipate and trigger worker bees—yes, plural, not just one—to start laying. Worker bees lay unfertilized eggs so **become drones only.**

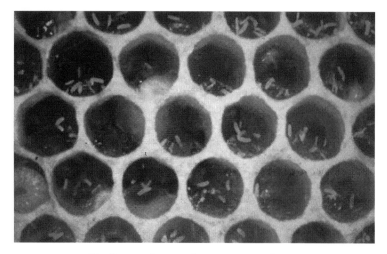

*Laying workers **will lay several eggs in a cell.** The eggs will settle on the cell sides. A new queen may also lay several eggs in a cell as she gets the hang of laying. (Courtesy The Animal and Plant Health Agency (APHA), Crown Copyright)*

How to tell if you have laying workers? Worker bees **will lay several eggs in one cell** as opposed to the one egg per cell laid by a queen bee. The eggs will also **stick to the side of the wax cell** since worker bees can't reach the cell center like a queen bee can.

To remedy laying workers, you can:

- Add **a frame of brood** with young 1 to 3 day eggs so bees have eggs they can raise into a queen.
- **Try to re-queen.** Some colonies will reject a new queen since they have worker bees filling in for her.
- **Unite queenless colony** with a stronger colony. The stronger colony will drive out laying workers.

HOW TO REQUEEN

Queen suppliers usually offer both virgin (unmated) queens and mated queens. Make **sure you know which ones you are getting** when ordering queens. Mated queens cost more than virgin ones.

A virgin queen has very little to no unique pheromone. Once settled into a new colony, she will need to fly to a drone congregation area to mate with 15-20 drones, then make a safe flight home before she starts laying. If she doesn't first become a bird snack, laying can take 2-4 weeks depending on weather.

A mated queen is ready to start laying once she settles into the new colony. She has a unique pheromone and can quickly get the colony back on track within 1-2 weeks from getting settled.

Queen suppliers also ship queen bees in different cages. Some have only a cork plug

Queen bees usually travel with an **entourage of worker bees inside the queen cage. If queen is mated,** *outside worker bees will pick up on queen pheromone and start spreading it through colony.*

at the release end; others have sugar plugs that keep the queen and entourage fed. **Ask the supplier how he is shipping the queen.**

INTRODUCING A NEW QUEEN BEE

Remove all queen cells from the receiving colony including the **tiny emergency queen cells**. If they still have any sort of queen cell on frames, worker bees can hypothetically use the emergency cells to raise a new queen and may tend to reject a new introduced queen.

If you had a queen in the colony, it's best to leave the colony **queenless for 5-7 days** before introducing a new queen. By then the old queen pheromone will have dissipated and worker bees will want to welcome a new queen. This can get tricky with timing when the new queen(s) arrive.

New queen bee in a cage in hand, make sure she has **a candy plug in one end of the cage.** Some suppliers now ship queen bees with only corks and without a retinue to care for the queen.

If it only has a cork, carefully remove and add a small marshmallow to give the queen bee food without releasing her. Be careful, she can be quick!

When introducing her to the colony, place the queen cage between frames with the **wire mesh facing bees, NOT the frame.** You want the workers to quickly pick up her pheromone and to start grooming and feeding her through the cage mesh.

By the fourth day, workers should have consumed the candy plug and been released into the hive. Leave her alone **for another 5-7 days** before checking frames to see signs of egg-laying.

HOW TO UNITE TWO COLONIES

- Cover the inner cover of a strong colony hive with **one sheet of double page newspaper.**
- **Cut 6-9 small slits** in newspaper to help colony pheromones mingle.
- **Place weak hive box** on **top of newspaper.**
- **Provide upper entrance** for weak hive so bees can fly in and out. This can be a notched inner cover, an Imirie shim or some other homemade device.
- **Cover** the top of the weak hive box.
- **Wait a couple of days.** Check that the bees have chewed through newspaper and are freely moving between boxes.

*Combining two colonies is all about **giving pheromones first time to mingle.***

CATCHING "FREE BEES" OR SWARMS

ABOUT SWARMS

A swarm's life span is about **5 days.**

- **Normally the old queen** leads ½ of the colony, leaving a daughter behind to keep the main colony going. If the old queen is damaged, the daughter may lead the swarm.
- After the primary swarm, a colony may have several smaller **"after swarms"** when other new queens emerge. After swarms have unmated queens.
- Swarms may include *Varroa* mites and small hive beetles so they are **not pest free.**

Swarms are nature's way of ensuring bees reproduce. **Bees initiate swarm preparations when they are pressed for room.**

- Approximately **half of all swarms** don't make it through their first winter in a hive.
- Swarms require **active feeding** to get them established in their first year in a hive.

SWARM CALL LISTS

One of the ways you can get notified about swarms is to **get on swarm call lists.** Make sure you are available and responsive; many of these are emergency response organizations and they won't call you again if they can't reach you the first time:

- Fire dept. (city & rural)
- Police departments
- Animal Control
- Master gardeners
- Exterminators/pest control
- Local nurseries
- Extension office
- Master naturalists

Local and state bee clubs also often have a list; you usually have to join or be a member of those organizations to have your name included on their swarm call lists.

SIGNS OF COLONY SWARM PREPARATION

Worker bees tend to build swarm cells on frame bottoms. A swarm queen cell looks like a long peanut. Once the swarm queen cell is capped, swarming can take place any day.

- If preparing to swarm, **worker bees will stop** drawing wax comb on frames.
- Worker bees will stop feeding the older queen **to slim her down** so she can fly again with departing bees. If the older queen is injured or can't fly, the swarm may leave with the virgin queen.

SWARM TRAPS

Swarm traps can be as simple as a nuc box baited with a frame of old comb and food grade lemongrass essential oil to specially-made 40-inch deep swarm trap boxes.

The best place to locate a swarm trap is where **a swarm was caught in the past**.

Locate swarms at approximate **10-12 feet** in a tree or structure bees can easily access.

Bait with a frame of wax. A couple drops of food grade lemongrass essential oil may also get a Scout bee's attention.

HOW TO CATCH A SWARM

Beekeepers call it **the "unicorn" of swarm catching.** It's when a swarm moves into woodenware just sitting in the yard, or the back of your truck. That does happen but not very frequently!

If you want to try to catch swarms, it's helpful to have **extra hive equipment handy**. Swarms can be quite large and require a deep box; after swarms can be smaller and easily fit a nuc box.

Being ready to catch a swarm has a **swat team** feel to it. You should have a swarm-catching kit in your vehicle so you can quickly respond to calls.

SWARM CATCHING EQUIPMENT CHECK LIST

- ☐ Bee suit and gloves
- ☐ Hive
- ☐ Frame with drawn comb
- ☐ Frame of honey
- ☐ Spray bottle with 1:1 sugar syrup
- ☐ Loppers in case you need to cut down a tree branch
- ☐ Queen catcher
- ☐ White bed sheet
- ☐ Other:

_____

_____

Once a swarm location is identified, **you need to know:**

- What do they look like, can the finder send a photo?
- Are they indeed honey bees?
- Where are they located? Do you need a ladder to reach?
- How high off the ground are they?
- How long have they been there?
- Whose property are they on?
- Do you have property owner's permission to go on the property?
- What else, if anything, needs to be removed to get to the swarm?

Before working the swarm, **ask observers to move away** to a safe area.

If you can easily see it, try to **locate the queen.** Secure the queen in a queen catcher and place her in the hive box.

Move the hive box next to the swarm.

- Add frame of drawn comb.
- Add frame of honey when possible.

- Spray other frames with 1:1 sugar water.
- Add an inner cover and lid.
- Add the queen in a queen catcher.

Wait until the queen pheromone starts guiding bees into the hive box. **Wait for the bees** to move in on their own; one of Mother Nature's more amazing sights!

Once bees are in, **close up the entrance** and move hive to their new home.

You may need to **leave the hive until dusk** to catch all of the scout and foraging bees.

Feed the swarm with sugar syrup **to encourage them to stay.**

IF YOU CAN'T FIND THE SWARM QUEEN

1. **Close the hive entrance.**
2. **Spread white sheet** on ground under swarm.
3. Add a frame of **old drawn comb** and a **frame of honey** if you have it. If not, spray the empty frames with sugar syrup.
4. **Place the hive as close to the swarm as you can.** Gently move the swarm into the box or move the box closer to the swarm until the bees fall gently into the box.
5. **Observe if bees are moving into the hive**; you may have secured the queen.

AFTER SWARM CATCHING CARE TIPS

To encourage colony **to stay in their new home:**

- Give colony **frame of capped and uncapped brood.**
- Provide a frame of honey.
- Feed **1:1 sugar syrup** inside nuc or hive box.
- Add queen excluder to box top. If worker bees flying out, you don't have queen. Remove queen excluder.
- **Reduce entrance** to discourage robbing.
- **If swarm seems unsettled,** close up the nuc or hive box for 1-2 days; no more than 3 days in one stretch. Bees need to relieve themselves.

As swarm settles in:

- **Monitor** for eggs.

- Monitor egg-laying pattern; 50% of swarms need to be requeened.
- If you can't easily find a queen, **merge colony** with another hive. Divide later when queens are available.

NOT ALL SWARMS STAY

Don't take it personally if the swarm doesn't stay. It means scout bees found a location the colony preferred before you offered them a new home.

If the colony has swarmed again and is easy to reach, try to re-hive. **Adding a frame of open brood** from another colony may encourage bees to stay. The nurse bees will want to care for the open brood.

SWARM TRAPS

There are a variety of swarm trap designs. The easiest swarm trap is to **bait a nuc box with old comb** and a **couple drops of food grade lemongrass,** which simulates the smell of honey.

Place the swarm trap in a tree or 10-12 feet off the ground. The best place to catch a swarm is **where a swarm was caught the year before.**

If this is your first try at catching swarms, **place it 10-12 feet off the ground and safely secured for both your and bees safety.**

*Some **swarm traps can double** as beginning colony homes.*

HOW TO INSTALL A NUC AND FULL COLONY

Work with the colony supplier on timing. The colony should be **closed up the night before** it is going to be moved or early morning before sunrise so you are picking up most of the foragers.

- **Strap the colony down** so the lid and bottom board don't move.
- **Take a laundry bag** to cover the nuc in case any bees escape. May make your drive home less exciting.
- Set up the hive stand location.
- Move the hive to the hive stand location.

- Open the sealed entrance and **add greenery** over the entrance so bees know to re-orient themselves.
- **Let the colony settle in** for about a week before opening the hive.
- This works for both nucs and full colonies.

BEARDING

*One of the first behaviors that throws new beekeepers is called **"bearding."** Worker bees will hang out on the outside of the hive to help moderate the inside hive temperature usually mid-summer. To help cool the hive, place a small piece of wood under the telescoping cover to encourage the chimney effect pulling air through the colony.*

WALKAWAY SPLITS

Beginning colonies such as package bees and nucs will spend **their first year making wax** and, hopefully, collecting resources to have enough stored winter food. There are instances when purchased established colonies quickly expand.

To manage the quick expansion, the new colony may need to be split. As a beginning beekeeper, the easiest way to divide a colony is with a **walkaway split.**

1. Set up the second hive **facing the opposite direction** of the first hive.
2. **Divide the colony frames** between the two hives filling the empty space with new empty frames.
3. Make sure **both colonies have frames of capped and uncapped brood** and at least one frame of brood with eggs (1-3 days old) so bees can raise a new queen. They also need enough nurse bees to cover the frames.
4. Close up the hive; **check back in a week to 10 days** to determine which hive has the current queen. The hive with new eggs has the queen. Check for queen cells.
5. **Within 3 hours** the other hive should be **raising a new queen.**

NOTCHING A FRAME FOR QUEEN-REARING

This is simplified but you may hear of "notching a frame." This is one way to encourage bees to **easily raise a new queen.**

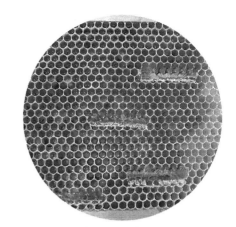

To **notch the frame** of brood with young larvae, select a frame with the youngest larvae in royal jelly, which basically are larvae most can't see. Look for the royal jelly. You want larvae that are **3 days old or less.**

To notch, take your hive tool and **gently pull the wax** from under a cell with a teeny tiny larvae. Gently push the hive tool into the foundation.

This is a frame demonstrating **notching under cells with day old larvae.**

Return the notched frame to a queenless hive.

Some beekeepers return to hive 4-5 days later, confirm bees are raising queen cells at the notches, and remove any other queen cells that may be forming.

MOVING HIVES OR THE "TWO TWO" RULE

If you need to relocate your hives:

- Move the hive when the temperature is **50°F or more.**
- Move the hive a **few inches every day,** no more than two feet at a time, until you have it in the new location. Monitor that foragers are finding home as they return to the hive.
- Move the hive **at least 2 miles** from the old location and leave them **for 3 weeks,** the expected life span of a forager. Now all foragers arriving at the new location, in theory, have no history with the surroundings. Return them to their new location.
- Close them up at night both ways so you don't lose foragers. When returning them, **add greenery over the entrance** to prompt them to re-orient themselves to the new location.

In all cases, suit up; make sure the hive is secure before moving.

GETTING READY FOR WINTER!

Helping your bees through their first winter with you is exciting.

- It gives you time to **catch your breath** and think about what you learned.

- It marks the **beginning of your first full year with bees.**

- And if you are successful, in our bee club you get to **officially call yourself a beekeeper!**

Over Wintering Basics

☐ Each colony needs at least **50-80 lbs of honey** on hand.

☐ Colonies monitored for *Varroa* mite levels; **compare to previous** *Varroa* **mite checks** to benchmark mite levels.

☐ Colonies are treated with oxalic acid vapor when colony is without brood **2 weeks after hard frost** through the end of the year, when conditions are right.

☐ **Hive lids secured** so they don't fly off in high winds.

- Ratchet Straps
- Bungee Cords
- Concrete blocks
- Rocks

*Keep entrance reducers **cleared of ice and snow** so bees can take cleansing flights on warm days. Good hive ventilation is important all year to prevent moisture accumulation inside hives.*

Optional Over Wintering

- ☐ **Hives are wrapped** (black roofing felt)
  - Protects hive against winter winds and
  - Helps absorb sun to raise inside hive temperature.

- ☐ **Hives are insulated** (foam board, insulated black plastic wraps)
  - Slows loss of hive heat

- ☐ Hives have **an upper entrance:**
  - Reduces moisture accumulation and
  - Gives bees a second exit in case lower entrance gets blocked.

- ☐ **Supplemental sugar cake feeding** over the cluster:
  - Emergency food
  - Hive condensation and moisture control
  - Spray lightly with water to keep sugar cake easily accessible to bees.

- ☐ Screened top inner covers replaced with **solid inner covers.**

- ☐ Entrance reducers turned to **single bee size entry to reduce drafts.**

- ☐ **Frames with empty wax comb stored** in sealed containers with Paradichlorobenzene crystals. One tablespoon tied up in a coffee filter per sealed container will discourage wax moths.
  - Don't place this product into an occupied hive; air out equipment used with this product derivative before placing back into hives.
  - Product examples: ParaMoth™ and "Moth Ice Crystals."
  - **DO NOT USE MOTH BALLS,** they contain naphthalene that leaves a residue on the beekeeping equipment that will kill your bees.

- ☐ **Quilt Boxes** filled with straw or cedar shavings can help absorb moisture a winter cluster produces.

- ☐ Other

HONEY BEE CLUSTERS

Honey bees don't hibernate; they **cluster around the queen** while worker bees rotate among themselves to stay warm.

They also **don't heat the whole hive**; they concentrate only on keeping themselves warm in basically a tight wad.

To locate a winter cluster, place your bare hand under the inner cover and over frames and feel the hot spot. That's where the cluster will be located.

Small hive beetles will winter over inside the cluster.

TEMPERATURE IMPACTS ON CLUSTERED BEES	
64 °F	Bees begin to cluster inside the hive; **optimum cluster temperature 95°F.**
57 °F	Bees don't move in the outer shell but are still moving inside the cluster. • Minimum inner cluster 55°F. • Minimum outside cluster shell 46°F.
45 °F	**Bee bodies will be unable to move** when their body temperature reaches 45°F and below. They will freeze to death at 32°F.
44 °F +	Bees will break cluster to take cleansing flights and defecate outside their hives.
41 °F	Cluster can cover 8-10 frames.
23 °F	Outer bees start moving their wing muscles to generate heat.
7 °F	Cluster can cover 5-6 frames.
-5 °F	Cluster may only cover 2-3 frames.

So. For those of you who **just can't stay out of your hives during winter** (yes, we know who you are, the bees will tell on you!)

COLONY CHECKING AND INSPECTING TEMPERATURE GUIDE

*(Listed temperatures are without wind chill. In general,
don't inspect your hives when it's windy)*

During winter **do not open hives and break propolis seals.** Bees won't have time to reseal and produce more propolis.

Below 30 °F	**Open hive only in an emergency** (to feed and remove chemicals.) If need to feed, use dry sugar or candy so food doesn't freeze.
Below 40 °F	Open hive **only in emergency.** Move hand over top of frames to feel cluster heat. Place supplemental feed immediately over cluster.
Below 50 °F	Bees loosely clustered and making cleansing flights. Remove side frames to check brood frames but **do not remove brood frames** or they may get chilled.
55 °F	Bees will be flying and foraging if food available. **Hive can be opened** but **brood frames should be left in** so that they are not chilled.
60 °F	Complete hive inspection can be done but **brood frames need to be inspected and quickly returned back to the hive.**
70 °F	**Warm enough to conduct a full hive inspection** without chilling brood frames.
74 °F	If other conditions are right, plants start to **entice pollinators with nectar-production.** This is the beginning of the flow.
86 °F	Plants stop producing nectar and pollen and go into survival mode. **Bees will turn to alternate food sources** such as hummingbird feeders, cracked corn, etc. Opening hives for inspection may prompt robbing from nearby hives.

REMINDER WHEN NOT TO OPEN YOUR COLONIES

Periodically a beginning beekeeper will try to "negotiate" when they want to inspect their colonies. It's not negotiable, **hives should not be opened and inspected when temperatures are 45°F or colder.** If you **need to check a colony:**

- Quickly open the lid,
- Move your hand around to locate the cluster warm and/or
- Peer down through the frames. Use flashlight if necessary.
- Do not break the propolis seals keeping the hive bodies protected.
- In other words, **stay out of your hives in winter!**

DO NOT OPEN YOUR HIVES WHEN:

1. *A weak colony is being robbed.*
   - Close up the hive including the entrance.
   - Discourage robbers with a water spray bath.
   - Move the colony under attack and install a robbing screen.
   - Cover hive with a damp cloth/sheet but leave a bee exit. Monitor for decreased robbers.

2. *When your bees are cranky.*
   - Close them back up; your bees are cranky most likely for a good reason, starting with being out of food, out of room, or without a queen.
   - Get back there with a smoker and determine what's bothering them.

3. *When you are in a rush. You will kill more bees and get more stings when you are not calm and patient. Slow down!*

4. *When it is overcast, raining and/or windy.* Bees will not be pleased when you take the lid off their home.

DARN. WHEN YOU LOSE YOUR BEES...

Heartbreaking. There's no better word to describe that moment when you open your hive and realize your bees are gone. For good.

Don't allow them to die in vain; **learn from it.** The following are some of the **main reasons why bees die** in the first few years of beekeeping:

MAIN REASON HONEY BEES DIE

CAUSE	SYMPTOMS	NEXT TIME
Starvation: the colony was short of stored honey to make it through winter and/or cluster was too small to allow bees to reach honey close by.	Worker bees, in a cluster, found head first in wax comb cells with back sides sticking up.	• Leave bees extra honey for winter. • Add supplemental sugar cakes or candy board at hive top. • Check supply through winter. Provide more if necessary.
Varroa Mites: **Strong colony makes it through winter** only to die late February/early March.	*Varroa* mite numbers keep increasing through fall as bee numbers decrease. Beekeeper doesn't take steps to manage *Varroa*. The colony collapses in late winter.	• **Monitor** *Varroa* mite levels. • Manage for *Varroa*. • When *Varroa* mite levels are 1+ per 100 bees, consider treatment options for *Varroa*.
"Rolling the Queen" Colony was growing nicely; numbers start going down and queen can't be found.	Killing the queen as you are rapidly removing frames.	• Locate queen; set her aside **in nuc** when inspecting. • **Take your time removing frames.**

CAN YOU REUSE YOUR BEEKEEPING EQUIPMENT?

Yes, if the bees didn't die from a communicable disease. **Confirm the cause of death** before re-using equipment.

Sterilize tools before going from one colony to the next.

Work with your mentor and/or local bee club to do a "dead out" visual autopsy. Discuss symptoms and what were the possible causes.

Learn from each loss and become a better beekeeper.

GOOD TO KNOW
TIP

*You can also buy some used beekeeping equipment. **Ask first why the beekeeper is selling and whether it has been exposed to any adverse conditions such as diseases.** Check that the hive body is sound and there are no rotting spots, you can always give it a new coat of paint. This is a migratory lid on this nuc; doesn't have or need an inner cover. And there's no substitute for experienced equipment!*

Your Notes

_____

_____

_____

_____

_____

_____

_____

_____

_____

Your Notes

_____

_____

_____

_____

_____

_____

_____

_____

_____

CHAPTER 7

Honey Bee Pests & Diseases

MAJOR CHANGES IN MANAGING PESTS AND DISEASES

Prior to 2017, some beekeepers depended on applying antibiotics to their colonies "just in case." As a result of the overuse of antibiotics, we now have superorganism strains resistant to formerly effective medications, both in humans and livestock.

January 2017, the US Food and Drug Administration instituted the **Veterinary Feed Directive.** The law requires, among other things, for a veterinarian to first check honey bee hives to determine if the use of antibiotics is necessary. The veterinarian can then prescribe medication as needed.

Many established beekeepers I know took issue with this new directive. Some in my area started to stockpile antibiotics so they didn't need to work through a veterinarian. They now may be administering expired antibiotics.

Antibiotics disrupt the bees gut microbiome, where beneficial bacteria and fungi assure healthy larval growth and development. Much as humans focus on probiotics

*Honey bees **collect tree resin to produce propolis, a form of bee glue** with antibiotic properties that keep the colony healthy. It also makes it tough for beekeepers to open hives and separate hive bodies.*

for their gut health, beekeeping research emphasizes the importance of a healthy bee gut microbiome that can be destroyed by antibiotic overkill.

When I started beekeeping 10 years ago, I was advised to use antibiotics as a preventative and to remove the "bee glue," or propolis, because it got in my way. I did neither. Although little was known then about propolis's role in a hive, my theory was we may not know why but the bees make it for a reason. Dr. Marla Spivak's current research is increasingly bringing to light the **value of propolis in a colony's health.**

Dr. Spivak's research published in 2017 has concluded that the **propolis envelope bees build is a shield against American foulbrood (AFB)** *Paenibacillus larvae.* It "serves as an antimicrobial layer around the colony that helps protect the brood from bacterial pathogen infection, resulting in a lower colony-level infection load."

American foulbrood (AFB) is periodically confirmed in parts of Midwest. AFB spores are known to be viable in used hive equipment for up to 40 years. Although Canadian commercial beekeepers have developed a way to detoxify AFB-infected hive equipment, the most economically feasible approach for US hobby beekeepers is to replace the hive equipment and burn the contaminated ones. Also see page 163 for how to humanely dispatch bees.

Currently ongoing research is also focused on **Deformed Wing Virus (DWV)** one of the leading causes of honey bee colony losses.

DWV is suspected of causing wing and abdominal deformities often found on adult honeybees in colonies infested with *Varroa* mites. These symptoms include damaged appendages, particularly stubby, useless wings, shortened, rounded abdomens, mis-coloring and paralysis of the legs.

DWV was initially solely associated as a virus vectored by *Varroa* mites; now it's been determined DWV is much more genetically diverse in the US. The diversity will make it more complicated to develop virus treatments.

The best thing beekeepers can currently do to cut down DWV damage is to **limit virus levels.** Since the virus is transmitted through *Varroa* mites, treating for and reducing bees exposure to *Varroa* mites should cut down on DWV levels.

The bottom line is new beekeepers need to **manage *Varroa* mites** and **select bees with hygienic behavior,** ones that can detect disease and mite-ridden brood and remove the brood before it finishes developing.

FIRST THING TO DO IF YOU SUSPECT A PROBLEM

If you detect a weak hive, **immediately reduce the size of the entrance.** You want to give guard bees some help in protecting the colony from stronger colonies that may rob them.

It will also give you **a little time** to determine what is happening to the colony.

HONEY BEE PESTS AND DISEASES

The following are the three **main pests and diseases** currently identified and known to impact honey bees:

VARROA MITES
(Varroa destructor and Varroa jacobsoni)

See my April 2018 video of *Varroa* mites on drone brood comb:
bit.ly/Varroamites

Varroa destructor and *Varroa jacobsoni* are referred to, in general, as ***Varroa* mites.** These **parasitic mites** attach themselves to the underside of the bee's scales and feed off the bee's immune system, the "fat body" organ, leaving the worker and drone brood susceptible to the dozens of viruses the mites vector.

***Varroa* don't fly;** they are phoretic, dependent on foragers for rides and move from hive to hive through robbing and other "sharing." An untreated colony getting robbed by phoretic *Varroa* will create a *Varroa* bomb, increasing the mite population in nearby colonies.

Varroa is thought to have all but eliminated feral bee colonies in many areas and is present in most apiaries worldwide except Australia.

Colony Collapse Disorder was coined in 2006 by Florida State Bee Inspector Jerry Hayes to try to identify the huge losses of colonies across the US. Since then, the symptoms of Colony Collapse Disorder have been attributed to *Varroa* mites.

Today ***Varoosis*** refers to symptoms arising from heavy *Varroa* mite infestation. To date the mites vector, or transmit, dozens of debilitating viruses. If left unchecked, in general bee colonies will die within 2-3 years.

SYMPTOMS: WHAT YOU WILL SEE

Varroa multiply inside the **larger drone cells.** One female January 1 will become 1,000 by August.

During their mobile lifecycle stage, these external pests are visible with the naked eye and look like a **red or brown spot** on a bee's body, most easily visible on the head and thorax.

It can also be found **feeding between bee abdomen segments although those are harder for the naked eye to see.**

With a light infestation, there will be few symptoms.

When there is a **medium infestation,** mites will be found on drone brood and on the adult bee thorax.

Signs of a heavy infestation include greasy looking bees, a dwindling bee population, and deformed bees, the wings of which are shriveled up or completely missing (Deformed Wing Virus).

DWV is one of more than two dozen known viruses vectored by *Varroa* mites.

OPTIONS: *VARROA* MITE MANAGEMENT

Currently **it is not possible** to completely remove *Varroa* mites from colonies.

As a beekeeper, you are now basically managing two arthropods:

- Trying to keep honey bees healthy and safely housed inside hive bodies and
- Trying to keep *Varroa* mites out and low in numbers.

Using a combination of Integrated Pest Management, (IPM) beekeepers should maintain *Varroa* mite levels below the threshold affecting colony health, which changes depending on a number of factors.

Currently the threshold is **1 *Varroa* mite per 100 bees.**

Varroa mites may fall to the hive bottom whether treated or untreated. Monitoring is an important and effective tool to check on and track mite levels.

Integrated Pest Management (IPM) combines the pest life cycle, mechanical approaches such as drone removal and chemical/non-chemical treatments that work best for your colonies.

Varroa mite recommendations are also frequently updated based on the latest scientific research findings.

The most comprehensive, and up to date source of *Varroa* mite control recommendations is available through the Honey Bee Health Coalition.

Download their latest guide found here:
www.honeybeehealthcoalition.org

SMALL HIVE BEETLES (SHB)

(SHB) *Aethina tumida* can destroy a bee colony.

SHB **will quietly co-exist with a colony** until the colony releases stress pheromones high enough to trigger the female SHB to start laying eggs.

Each SHB female can lay 1,200 eggs a day.

Once hatched, larvae tunnel through the comb and leave excrement that causes fermented, runny honey.

Clusters of eggs laid in areas where bees cannot reach lead to thousands of aggressive larvae seeking pollen, bee larvae and pupae to eat.

SHB larvae have **three sets of larger, more pronounced legs located near the head.**
- SHB larvae burrow in soil below and around the hive where they pupate.
- SHB larvae don't mind being exposed to sunlight.
- SHB adults will tickle nurse bees to prompt feeding.
- **SHB adults can fly up to 7 miles** and will travel with swarms.
- They will also be **found inside winter clusters.**

SYMPTOMS: WHAT YOU WILL SEE

Adult black beetles about the size of a ladybug are usually found inside hive lid, moving over comb and under supplemental food including sugar syrup feeding jars and protein patties. Their trophallactic behavior, tickling nurse bees, provides them with food.

Strong hives often are able to keep adult SHB trapped in nooks and crannies to the point where beetles are unable to reproduce.

Weaker, stressed colonies produce a high-stress pheromone level that triggers female adult SHB to lay eggs.

Growing SHB larvae can be found in hive debris in the bottom of the hive, along frame top and bottom ridges and in any other dark, protected places.

SHB larvae may also appear in supplemental protein patties hatching underneath protein patties.

SHB larvae have three legs at the front of their body, as opposed to wax moth larvae which have legs along the length of the similar-looking larvae.

In severe cases, developing larvae can be found infesting honey stores and "sliming" honey frames. SHB reproduction produces a **pungent, foul odor similar to dirty socks.**

When the infestation becomes **too great, bees will abandon the hive.**

OPTIONS: SHB TREATMENT

Remove "slimed" individual honey and pollen frames. **Put in freezer overnight** to kill existing SHB larvae and eggs.

Scratch wax caps and then, using a garden hose, gently flush out honey/dead brood without damaging delicate comb. Shake excess water from comb and return to hive after it is dry and of ambient temperature.

Check bottom board for SHB larvae in wax and collected debris. **Scrape onto newspaper;** roll it up and take it to a safe area to burn.

If you scrape debris into soil you are giving SHB a place to hatch.

Small hive beetle larvae sliming a honey frame. *(Photo courtesy of Gregg Hitchings)*

SHB PREVENTION

- **Maintain a large, strong colony with minimal stress.** Treat colonies for *Varroa*, which currently is the leading cause of colony stress.

- **Keep hives in direct sunlight;** shaded colonies will experience more SHB since SHB avoid light.

- **Use of SHB traps help to trap adult SHB.**

- Remove debris in hive bottom, especially in spring, freeze or burn; do not toss into soil. Larvae in soil will pupate into adult SHB.

Research has shown SHB larvae **will crawl fifty feet or more.**

You can also **treat your soil with nematodes** to eliminate SHB larvae in soil.

WAX MOTHS
(Achroia grisella) and *(Galleria mellonella)*

Two moths, **Lesser Wax Moth** *(Achroia grisella)* and the **Greater Wax Moth** *(Galleria mellonella)*

Wax moths do not directly harm bees but **can destroy unoccupied comb and woodenware.**

Wax moth larvae are a secondary predator of bee larvae and pupae and feed on beeswax, pollen and honey unless bees catch and remove them.

Strong hives will remove wax moth larvae and discourage wax moths from entering the hive. You will sometimes find **adults on the outside of a hive.**

Lesser Wax Moth, Photo Credit to Sarefo, CC BY-SA 3.0 via Wikimedia Commons

Greater Wax Moth, Photo Credit to Simon Hinkley & Ken Walker, Museum Victoria, CC BY 3.0 AU; via Wikimedia Commons

SYMPTOMS: WHAT YOU WILL SEE
White cocoons on the side and bottom of the hive; **spider-like webbing through comb.**

Before making the cocoon, larvae **bore scallops into the frames and woodwork.** They look like some ancient form of hieroglyphs.

Wax moth larvae emerging from white cocoons attached to the inside of a hive. Remove and feed wax moth larvae to birds, they are favorite bird hatchling food. (Photo courtesy of Gregg Hitchings)

In early stages, **wax moth larvae look similar to SHB larvae.** Wax moth larvae do not like sunlight.

How to tell the difference:

- SHB larvae have **three sets of legs close to the head.**
- Wax moth larvae have many **small, fleshy, uniform legs along the body length.**

Wax moth larvae,
http://bit.ly/2MoDYsS

HOW TO MANAGE

Freeze comb before storing.

Store empty frames in cool conditions; be careful moving because comb is fragile.

Para-Moth™ (paradichlorobenzene) can be used in tightly sealed woodenware to prevent wax moth damage.

- **Do not use moth balls!**
- **Do not use in hives.**

After winter storage, **air out frames for several days before placing back into hives** or the Para Moth™ will kill your bees.

WAX MOTH PREVENTION

Wax moths are opportunistic and move in when a colony is stressed and on the decline.

Keep colonies strong and healthy and the bees will keep wax moths from moving in.

EARLY WARNING

I consider wax moth signs as an early warning that something is not quite right with a colony. As soon as I see wax moths inside a hive, I inspect the colony to determine what may be going wrong.

Okay, those are the **three main pests** you need to know as a beginning beekeeper.

For those of you who want to know some of the other honey bee pest and disease threats, here are the others **in alphabetical order:**

MORE HONEY BEE PESTS & DISEASES

AMERICAN FOULBROOD (AFB)

Before parasitic mites, **American foulbrood was the most serious bee disease.**

AFB is caused by the **bacterium** *Paenibacillus larvae*.

AFB infected bee larvae is spread by spores that are consumed by larvae during their first couple of days in the cell.

One dead larvae may contain as many as **100 million spores.**

AFB spores are known to be viable for up to 40 years.

This is why beekeepers are told to ask someone selling used beekeeping equipment why they are selling.

AFB and European foulbrood are often confused with each other.

If you confirm your apiary has AFB, **notify other nearby apiaries as a courtesy. AFB is highly contagious.**

AFB with a toothpick in the wax.

SYMPTOMS: WHAT YOU WILL SEE

- **Spotty brood** pattern.
- Pupae die **after being capped; caps are sunken** and appear **greasy and wet.**
- Cell wax caps may also **be perforated.**
- Infected bee larvae will turn **dull white to tan to brown.**
- At the brown stage, when the cell is stirred with a toothpick and the **toothpick is removed, the cell content will appear "ropy."**
- Dead and dried pupae in the cell will also dry down to **scale in the bottom of the cell.**

- The hive will have a **chicken coop-like foul odor.**

To confirm suspected AFB cases, comb samples containing infected larvae **can be sent to a diagnostic lab** for no-cost testing.

- USDA Agricultural Research Service, Bee Research Lab At Beltsville, Maryland:
- **bit.ly/3qpVRXs**

AFB field kits are also readily available from bee equipment suppliers and some farm and home retailers.

OPTIONS: AFB TREATMENT

Burn all frames and comb; scorch boxes and other equipment.

Humanely kill bees in a water and dishwashing liquid solution.

If it is early in the season, an option is to kill the queen and shake all the bees onto new frames with new, undrawn foundation in a new hive.

Introduce a new queen bred for hygienic behavior and leave her caged for 3 days. Place the colony well away from others and feed a 1:1 (sugar:water) syrup to encourage comb building.

Monitor the colony closely to ensure brood rearing appears normal.

AFB PREVENTION

Keep strong healthy colonies headed by young prolific queens.

Varroa **Sensitive Hygiene (VSH)** queens show some AFB resistance.

After working with colonies suspected of having AFB, **sanitize hive tools and thoroughly wash hands and gloves** before moving onto the next colony.

Replace old combs on a regular basis; replace a third of all brood combs every year.

Don't leave old comb accessible to foraging bees.

CHALKBROOD
(Ascosphaera apis)

Chalkbrood is a fungus that attacks the honey bee larvae.

It appears when a bee colony is in distressed from **food shortages and erratic temperatures.**

Most cases of chalkbrood **appear in spring.** Long periods of rain can cause moisture build up.

- Chalkbrood **spreads by spores** from previous infections.
- Chalkbrood is contagious.

Remember to clean hive tool when moving from a contaminated hive to the next hive. Use alcohol or sterilize hive tool in smoker before using again.

SYMPTOMS: WHAT YOU WILL SEE

The brood, both sealed and unsealed, will have a **fuzzy, white growth** that almost looks like wool or cotton.

Photo credit to Jeff Pettis from United States, CC BY 3.0 US, **bit.ly/3iPemRZ**

- The larvae will then **harden into gray mummies.**
- **The hard, dead bodies** will be visible on hive floor or thrown out of hive entrance.
- Mummies will **vary in color** from a chalk white to a mixture of white and gray.

OPTIONS: CHALKBROOD TREATMENT

Chalkbrood is usually temporary and rarely fatal to a colony; most will recover without intervention.

If the disease persists, **re-queening is an effective way** to return the colony to health.

PREVENTION

- **Keep hives dry.**
- If one colony has chalkbrood, **sanitize hive tools** before moving onto the next colony.
- **Keep strong healthy colonies headed by young prolific queens.**
- **Replace one-third of your used apiary comb** each year.

EUROPEAN FOULBROOD (EFB)

European foulbrood (EFB) disease caused by the **bacteria** *Melissococus plutonius.*

It affects a colony when the **nectar flow is more sporadic, usually in spring.**

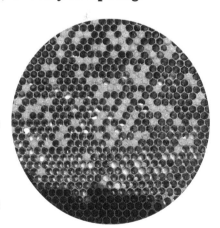

Spotty infected brood pattern (Photo courtesy of Gregg Hitchings)

EFB can be confused with AFB and vice versa:

- EFB **kills brood BEFORE they are capped.**
- **AFB kills brood after it is capped.**
- Sometimes **EFB signs will disappear during the onset of a good nectar flow.**
- Infected colonies must be closely monitored.

To confirm EFB, comb samples can be **sent to a diagnostics lab** for a no-cost final determination.

- USDA Agricultural Research Service, Bee Research Lab At Beltsville, Maryland:
- **bit.ly/3qpVRXs**

EFB field test kits are also available from bee equipment suppliers and some farm and home centers.

SYMPTOMS: WHAT YOU WILL SEE

- The EFB bacteria is fed to young larvae by nurse bees.
- The bacteria then compete(s) for nourishment inside the larvae, causing the **larvae to starve to death,** usually **before the cell is capped.**
- Infected larvae can appear **"deflated" and turn yellow to brown or dirty gray in color.**
- The spiracles of the tracheal system can appear as **"ribs" on the discolored larvae.**

(Photo courtesy of Gregg Hitchings)

- The other bacteria consume the larvae tissue until nothing is left but **a twisted, brown rubbery mess** that is usually curled upward at the bottom of the cell.
- **There may also be a foul odor.**

EFB TREATMENT

- **Simulate a nectar flow by feeding bees 1:1 (sugar:water) syrup for 2-3 weeks.**
- It problems persist, kill the queen bee and shake remaining bees onto new frames with undrawn foundation in a new hive.
- Re-queen.

EFB PREVENTION

EFB can re-occur if contaminated frames and hardware are used.

- **Get rid of any old equipment** that is suspected to have been contaminated.
- **Keep strong bee colonies.**
- **Re-queen yearly.**
- **Replace** any **worn woodenware.**
- After working colonies suspected with EFB, **sanitize hive tools.**
- **Thoroughly wash hands and gloves** before moving onto the next colony.
- **Replace old comb on a regular basis.**
- **Don't leave old comb out** where foraging bees can get to it.

This is the most widespread adult bee disease. It is spread by spores of two *microsporidia.*

NOSEMA

- *Nosema apis* is primarily a problem in winter and early spring;
- *Nosema ceranae* affects bees in summer and fall.

Beekeepers are encouraged to stay current on scientific research concerning how best to deal with Nosema.

WHAT YOU WILL SEE

Bees **defecating inside the hive** instead of flying outside.

Yellow to light brown streaks on the outside of the hive entrance.

The colony **may re-queen for no apparent reason.**

The infection causes the **queen's ovaries to degenerate, causing laying issues.**

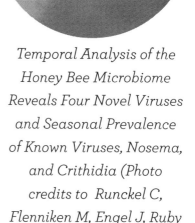

Temporal Analysis of the Honey Bee Microbiome Reveals Four Novel Viruses and Seasonal Prevalence of Known Viruses, Nosema, and Crithidia (Photo credits to Runckel C, Flenniken M, Engel J, Ruby J, Ganem D, Andino R, DeRisi J.; **bit.ly/2YhPBED***)*

NOSEMA TREATMENT

In the past, beekeepers were sometimes advised to routinely treat colonies with Fumagillin®.

Recent research has strongly called this practice into question as the disadvantages outweigh advantages.

NOSEMA PREVENTION

Ensure bee colonies have healthy diets of pollen and nectar.

Control hive moisture by providing **appropriate ventilation.**

Routine **culling of old comb,** which provides the infection source, can help to eliminate Nosema spores.

ON THE HORIZON

TROPILAELAPS MITES

Tropilaelaps Mites (Photo credit to Denis Anderson, CSIRO) **bit. ly/3prYCXE**

Smaller, more slender body than *Varroa.*

At least four species:

- *T. thaii*
- *T. Koenigerum*
- *T.clareite*
- **T.mercedesae* (*the biggest threat to managed bees.)

Not currently found in US but has spread from Asia, where it is more prevalent than *Varroa,* to Afghanistan, Papua New Guinea, and Korea.

WHAT YOU WILL SEE

Currently compared to *Varroa;* has major differences:

- This mite makes **many holes in a developing bee to feed instead of just a few.**
- **Re-infests brood cells within days.**
- Causes **significant brood death.**
- **Coexists with** *Varroa.*

OPTIONS

Other bee species have evolved natural strategies.

Researchers are trying to identify how they are surviving winter.

There is **currently no recommended** treatment.

OPTIONS TO DEAL WITH HONEY BEE PESTS AND DISEASES

Honey Bee Health Coalition Varroa Management Guide:

https://honeybeehealthcoalition.org/varroa

*This is old drone comb opened April 2018. Even though no Varroa were visible then on flying bees, **you can see Varroa inside drone comb** multiplying and feeding off drone pupae. Integrated pest management (IPM) is a tiered system using a pest's life cycle and common sense practices to be environmentally-sensitive, minimize chemical use and keep pest levels below damaging thresholds.*

VARROA MITE: INTEGRATED PEST MANAGEMENT

PROPOSED ACTION	NOTES
☐ Keep hives **staggered at least 5 feet+ apart,** not lined up in tight rows.	
☐ **Monitor** *Varroa* mite levels with mite counts through: *Powdered sugar shake*, Alcohol Wash** *3+ mites per ½ cup (300) bees requires beekeeper to develop a mite management plan.	
☐ **Remove drone comb** ☐ **Screened bottom boards** (10% effective) ☐ **Split colonies;** keep colonies small. ☐ **Create brood break** by temporarily caging queen ☐ **Re-queen from hygienic behavior colonies.** ☐ **Maintain strong, healthy colonies.** Destroy sick colonies so they don't spread mites. ☐ **Leave propolis to maintain colony health.** ☐ Supplement feed internally. **Do not open feed** and encourage robbing and increased exposure to *Varroa* mite-vectored viruses.	

- ☐ Treat with appropriate *Varroa* mite treatments suitable for weather conditions. **READ DIRECTIONS FOR CORRECT APPLICATION TIMES.**** Follow directions!

  ***More and more frequently is not better; apply **only** as directed.*

- ☐ **Use oxalic acid vapor or dribble once a year two weeks after the first hard fall frost** when colony is broodless through the end of the year, as appropriate.***

  ***There are other options for oxalic, do your homework and follow directions.

- ☐ **Replace old comb every 3-5 years.**

- ☐ **Other:**

VARROA MITE MONITORING

Both these methods are helpful to benchmark and monitor your *Varroa* mite population. **Sugar shakes and alcohol washes are NOT natural options to manage for *Varroa*.** When used on a regular basis, benchmarking *Varroa* mites in your hives **will help you determine what *Varroa* management options** you should pursue for best results. It will also help gauge what success you are having with the choices you are making.

TABLE 1: Treatment Thresholds per 300 (1/2c) bees

Colony Phase	Acceptable # of mites	Caution # of mites	Danger # of mites
Dormant with Brood	3	4-5	6+
Dormant without Brood	3	4-8	9+
Population Increase	3	4-8	9+
Peak Population	6	7-14	15+
Population Decrease	6	7-8	9+

Acceptable: *mite population are not an immediate threat.* **Caution:** *mite population may soon cause damage; non-chemical control my be employed, continue to sample and be ready to treat.* **Danger:** *Colony loss is likely unless beekeeper contols Varroa mites immediately.*

Table 1 credits: adapted from Honey Bee Health Coalition https://honeybeehealthcoalition.org/varroa/

SUGAR SHAKE OR SUGAR ROLL

The idea is simple: **you are dusting your bees with confectioner's sugar.** As bees groom themselves to remove the sugar, they will also be removing attached *Varroa* mites.

To make confectioner's sugar, **grind up regular sugar** to a fine dust in a blender or other similar kitchen appliance. You will need about half a cup for every 300 bees you sample.

Prepare a pint jar with a screen top holding bees in but allows sugar to gently shake out of the jar.

1. Prepare a mason jar lid by removing the inner seal and replacing it with a wire mesh. Keep the inner seal on.

2. **Mark the ½ cup level** on the side of the mason jar with a pen.

3. Gently run a mason jar lip **down the back of nurse bees** from top to bottom, tumbling bees into the mason jar. Trust me, it works!

4. Place lid with inner seal on. Gently—and I mean *gently*—shake the bees for 30 seconds to coat. You can also gently roll the jar to coat the bees.

5. Set jar aside for **3-5 minutes** to allow bees to try to remove the sugar and, by association, *Varroa* mites.

6. Remove inner seal. **Gently shake** sugar onto a white surface. Count the number of mites you see, those are the red dots.

7. Do it again with another serving of sugar with the same bees. Gently shake; set aside for 3-5 minutes.

8. Pour sugar onto a white surface. **Count the number of red dots**, which are *Varroa* mites.

9. You can return the nurse bees to the hive and their sisters will clean them up. Remember nurse bees don't fly so need to be returned to their colony.

10. Note your *Varroa* mite count in your diary so you have a benchmark.

Set up a schedule where you regularly monitor. Some do it once a month, others every other month. Make sure to check before you alter/treat your colony and afterwards to see if what you did impacted mite levels.

ALCOHOL WASH

An alcohol wash is also used as a *Varroa* mite count monitoring option. The process here **sacrifices ½ cup of bees, or approximately 300 bees,** to more accurately assess how many *Varroa* mites you have per hundred bees. Alcohol washes take less time than sugar rolls and are the most accurate way to determine mite load.

The general rule is **3 *Varroa* mites or less per 300 bees should be monitored.** Anything **over 1 *Varroa* mite per 100 may require management** to reduce the mite numbers; **9+ over per 300 bees requires immediate** and most probably ongoing treatment.

HOW TO DO AN ALCOHOL WASH

1. Prepare a mason jar lid by removing the inner seal and replacing it with a wire mesh. Keep the inner seal on.

2. **Mark the ½ cup level** on the side of the mason jar with a pen.

3. Gently run a mason jar lip **down the back of nurse bees** from top to bottom, tumbling bees into the mason jar or shake bees into container and scoop into jar.

4. **Pour alcohol into the jar to cover the bees.** (It will kill bees.) Shake 30 seconds.

5. Pour the **alcohol onto a white paint bucket lid** or other white surface.

6. Count the number of red dots, which are *Varroa* mites.

Refill same jar of bees with fresh alcohol; shake for 30 seconds. Pour on a white surface like a paint lid. Count the number of visible *Varroa*.

Keep good records so you can track mite numbers. **Note your *Varroa* mite count** and the date in your diary so you have a benchmark.

*Alcohol wash uses **½ cup of bees** to monitor Varroa mite levels.*

WHAT WE KNOW DOESN'T WORK FOR *VARROA*

Managing *Varroa* mites is constantly evolving. According to Jennifer Barry, University of Georgia Bee Lab, the following are scientifically confirmed approaches that **do not work:**

- Doing nothing.
- Letting bees die to eradicate inferior genes.
- Using smaller cell size foundation and bees.
- Top bar and Warre hives.
- Powdered sugar.
- Use of some chemical treatments (*Cumaphos:* Checkmite+™ and Tau-fluvalinate: Apistan ® strips)

WHAT IF I HAVE TO TREAT FOR *VARROA* MITES?

There are natural compound options and hard chemical options. Most have to be used in specific weather conditions and when honey supers are off. Read and follow label directions. Just because **it's natural doesn't mean it's good for bees.** Some natural compound options may leave residue in comb and impact bees.

In general:

- **Treat in Winter** with oxalic acid when colonies are broodless and all mites are out of the cells, usually 2 weeks to a couple of months after the last hard frost. Notes:

  _____

- **Treat in Spring and/or Fall** with a thymol or formic acid-based products when temperatures are within acceptable ranges. Notes:

  _____

- **Treat in Summer** with Apivar® during times when thymol, formic or oxalic acid may be ineffective (there is brood, it's too hot to use the product, etc. Notes:

  _____

After treating, especially in Summer, check *Varroa* mite levels to determine if the treatment(s) are working.

CURRENT ORGANIC *VARROA* MITE TREATMENT PRODUCTS

1. **Organic acid-based compounds that do not leave residues in the hive:**

   - *Oxalic Acid:* common in plants including tomatoes and rhubarb
   - *Formic Acid:* Mite Away Quick Strips™
   - *Hops beta acides*: Hopguard II™ extract from beer-making hops plants

2. **Extract oils that remain in wax comb but residues are unlikely to cause harm:**

   - *Apiguard ®*: Thymol gel: extract chemical from thyme.
   - *Thymol:* ApiVar® Life: extract chemical from thyme plus Camphor, menthol and Eucalyptol oil.

SHOULD I GO "TREATMENT FREE?"

You may have colonies with low *Varroa* mite counts one year but your neighbor's hives may have high counts, which may significantly impact both of your apiaries. Regardless of where you are in your beekeeping adventure, **monitor for *Varroa* mites.**

If you are a new beekeeper, **do not go "treatment free."**

- **You have many options** to manage *Varroa* mites without having to use chemicals.
- **Managing for *Varroa* mites** will help you familiarize yourself with this major colony impact.
- It will also provide a number of opportunities to **develop basic bee management techniques.**

If you are more experienced, don't go "treatment free" either.

- Your **lack of initiative** in managing *Varroa* mites **will impact other beekeepers, and hives,** around you.
- You can learn to manage *Varroa* by using hygienic queens, monitoring, removing drone comb and making splits.

The **Honey Bee Health Coalition has an excellent online decision tool** that will guide you through steps in deciding what to do about *Varroa* mites: **https://honeybeehealthcoalition.org/varroatool**

SMALL HIVE BEETLE TRAP HOMEMADE LURE RECIPE

You can buy small hive beetle lure and you can **make your own.** This has worked well for me over the years, making good use of banana peels.

- ½ cup apple cider vinegar
- ¼ cup sugar
- 1 cup water
- 1 ripe banana **peel** (not including banana) cut up finely

Replace when full of beetles every few days, depending on weather. The hotter the weather, the more frequent lure should be replaced.

Combine all ingredients in a glass jar. **Mark the jar to prevent unplanned sampling.**
Allow to ferment for 2 weeks in refrigerator.

Fill center of reusable and/or disposable small hive beetle traps; fill side traps ⅓ full of mineral or vegetable oil.

Place two traps per box. In summer, at opposite diagonal corners (left) and reverse as boxes added. **In winter, place traps in the hive box center.**

Replace when full of beetles every few days, depending on weather. The hotter the weather, the more frequently the lure should be replaced.

WAX MOTH HOMEMADE LURE RECIPE

- 1 cup water
- ½ cup vinegar
- 1 cup sugar
- 1 banana peel

Mix and place in 1 gallon jug with a one-inch hole cut near the top. Hang from a tree.

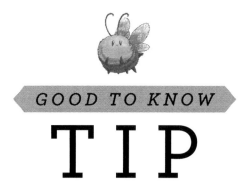

GOOD TO KNOW

TIP

*Ants may establish themselves on the inside cover of a hive, especially during wet springs. Deter ants by **sprinkling fresh ground cinnamon** around the edge of the inner cover. Ants will not bother the colony but may greatly aggravate the beekeeper!*

Your Notes

_____

_____

_____

_____

_____

_____

_____

_____

_____

Your Notes

CHAPTER 8

Safety First!

WHY HONEY BEES STING

Worker bees **sting when they perceive a threat** to themselves and their colony. Worker bees sting once, then die.

- Drone bees don't have a sting.
- Queen bees do but usually only sting other queens.
- You will **get stung the most as you get started.**
- **Take your time** when working with your bees.
- If you get stung, take that as a guide that you did something wrong.
- As you **learn how to better handle your bees, you should get stung less.**

It would take **1,100 bee stings to produce enough venom to be fatal to the average person. Monitor first stings** to determine your level of sensitivity/allergies.

Worker bees leave a sac of venom when they sting. The sac continues to pump venom unless you scrape it off. Don't pinch it or you will push more venom. ***Use hive tool to quickly remove by scraping the sac off.***

HOW TO SAFELY REMOVE BEE STINGS

This is a combination of beekeeper experience and advice from the Mayo Clinic:

1. **Don't panic.** Take a deep breath and pay attention to what bees are telling you.
2. Walk away from hive.
3. Locate the area with sting.
4. Use a **fingernail or hive tool and scrape stinger** out of your skin.
5. **Do not squeeze stinger,** you will be pushing more venom under your skin.
6. Rub with soil or talcum powder **to mask sting pheromone.**
7. Wash with soap and water.
8. Add cold compress.
9. If you have plantain nearby that hasn't had contact with pesticides and fertilizers, you can chew the leaves and apply the mashed leaves to the sting site to manage inflammation.
10. Sometimes bees may repeatedly sting your gloves because pheromones have accumulated through use. That's a good reminder you need to **wash your gloves!**

MAYO CLINIC TREATMENT FOR MODERATE STING REACTIONS

1. Remove the stinger as soon as possible; **scrape stinger off** with fingernail or hive tool.
2. **Wash the affected area** with soap and water.
3. Apply a **cold compress.**
4. Take an over-the-counter **pain reliever as needed**. You might try ibuprofen (Advil®, Motrin IB®, others) to help ease discomfort.
5. If the sting is on an arm or leg, **elevate it.**
6. Apply **hydrocortisone cream or calamine lotion** to ease redness, itching or swelling.
7. If itching or swelling is bothersome, **take an oral antihistamine** that contains diphenhydramine (Benadryl®) or chlorpheniramine.
8. **Avoid scratching the sting area.** This will worsen itching and swelling and increase your risk of infection.

LOCALIZED VS. SYSTEMIC ALLERGIC REACTION

A bee **sting bump** is a **localized reaction.**

An anaphylactic reaction is one that impacts your body and **can be life-threatening.**

According to the Mayo Clinic, anaphylaxis symptoms usually occur within minutes of exposure to an allergen. Sometimes, however, it can occur a half-hour or longer after exposure. **Signs and symptoms include:**

- Skin reactions, including hives and itching and flushed or pale skin
- Low blood pressure (hypotension)
- Constriction of your airways and a swollen tongue or throat, which can cause wheezing and trouble breathing
- A weak and rapid pulse
- Nausea, vomiting or diarrhea
- Dizziness or fainting

EMERGENCY ALLERGIC REACTION TREATMENT

During an anaphylactic attack, **an emergency medical team** may perform cardiopulmonary resuscitation (CPR) if someone stops breathing or the heart stops beating. The person may be given medications including:

- **Epinephrine (adrenaline)** to reduce body's allergic response
- **Oxygen,** to help with breathing
- **Intravenous (IV) antihistamines and cortisone** to reduce inflammation of air passages and improve breathing
- **A beta agonist (such as albuterol)** to relieve breathing symptoms

EPINEPHRINE AUTOINJECTOR

If you're **allergic to bee stings,** your doctor is likely to prescribe an emergency epinephrine autoinjector (EpiPen®, Auvi-Q®, others).

*Replace epinephrine pen **by its expiration date**. Consider wearing an allergy alert bracelet that identifies your bee allergy.*

Not all doctors will write a prescription for an autoinjector so check with your private physician.

- You'll need to **have it with you at all times**.
- An autoinjector is a combined syringe and concealed needle that injects a single dose of medication when pressed against your thigh.
- Be sure you know how to use the autoinjector. Make sure the people closest to you also know how to administer the drug and can guide you when you use the autoinjector.
- If you need to use the autoinjector, use it on yourself. **Keep it pressed for at least 2 seconds to administer the requisite dose.**
- Medical personnel called in to respond to a severe anaphylactic reaction also may give an epinephrine injection or another medication.
- If **someone else needs an autoinjector, guide their hand** so they are applying it to themselves.

ALLERGY SHOTS

Bee and other insect stings are a common cause of anaphylaxis. If you've had a serious reaction to a bee sting or multiple stings, your doctor likely will **refer you to an allergist** for allergy testing and consideration of allergy shots (immunotherapy).

These shots, generally given regularly for a few years, can reduce or eliminate your allergic response to bee venom.

IMMUNITY TO BEE STINGS

Over the years, I have found bee stings in Spring are more uncomfortable than stings later in the year. I have also found my **sensitivity to stings** has been **less as the years go by.**

BEFORE HEADING TO APIARY

Before heading into an apiary or field visit, spend a few minutes reviewing basic safety rules:

PRE-APIARY VISIT CHECK LIST - REMEMBER:

Take a deep breath. It will be ok!

- ☐ Check each other's suits, all zippers closed?
- ☐ Assign smoker caretakers
- ☐ Review how to safely approach a hive
- ☐ Location of fire extinguishers
- ☐ Location of First Aid Kit
- ☐ Anyone allergic to bee stings?
- ☐ Other:

_____

Have the following handy in your beekeeping bucket:

BEEKEEPING EMERGENCY CHECK LIST

- ☐ **Liquid antihistamine,** Faster absorption than pills
- ☐ **Antihistamine pills,** Easy to carry
- ☐ **Travel size talcum powder,** Mask sting pheromone
- ☐ **Adhesive bandages for cuts**
- ☐ **Water,** To clean cuts
- ☐ **Duct tape,** To seal bee suit rips
- ☐ **Other:**

_____

_____

GOOD TO KNOW
TIP

HONEY COUGH SYRUP RECIPE *(National Honey Board)*

Ingredients

- *Zest of 2 lemons (approx. 1½ T)*
- *1 cup water*
- *¼ cup ginger peeled, sliced or ½ tsp ground ginger*
- *1 cup honey*
- *½ cup lemon juice*

1. In a small saucepan, combine lemon zest, sliced ginger and 1 cup of water. Bring mixture to a boil, simmer for 5 minutes, then strain through into a heat-proof measuring cup.

2. Rinse the saucepan out and pour in 1 cup of honey. On low heat, warm the honey, but do not allow it to boil. Add the strained lemon ginger water and the lemon juice. Stir the mixture until it combines to form a thick syrup.

3. Pour into a clean jar with a lid.

Note: *This can be refrigerated for up to 2 months.*

For *children ages 1 to 5, use ½ to 1 tsp. every 2 hours. For children ages 5 to 12, use 1 to 2 tsp. every 2 hours. For children 12 and older and adults, use 1 to 2 T every 4 hours.

* Remember, honey is recommended for children over the age of one, not any younger.

Your Notes

_____

_____

_____

_____

_____

_____

_____

_____

_____

Your Notes

_____

_____

_____

_____

_____

_____

_____

_____

_____

CHAPTER 9
Hive Checks & Inspections

*Honey bees collect tree resin to produce propolis, **a form of bee glue with antibiotic properties that keep the colony healthy.** It also makes it tough for beekeepers to open hives and separate hive bodies.*

CHECKING VERSUS INSPECTING

There is a difference between checking and inspecting a colony.

- **Are your bees flying? A hive check** involves observing bees at the hive entrance; peeking under the outer cover and in general, making conclusions based on your observations of activities outside of the hive.

- **Did you see the queen*? A hive inspection** involves opening the hive and going frame by frame to observe, note and draw conclusions about what you actually see. *You don't need to see the queen to know the colony is queen-right, this is to help you remember the difference between a hive check and hive inspection.

*When starting, it helps to have **an extra set of hands** as you learn to balance frames with hive tool in your hand.*

Whenever going into your hives, **decide what you plan to do** before you open the hive.

- Have the beekeeping tools and equipment you need in hand;
- Be properly suited and
- Think through what you want to do before a lid is opened.

Detailed hive inspections usually include noting **how many brood frames are present;** what **kind of stores the colony has** and what, if anything, **the beekeeper needs to do next to help the colony.**

HIVE INSPECTIONS FREQUENTLY ASKED QUESTIONS

1. *What are you looking for in a general hive inspection?*

    - Bees **moving across frames** and **starting to draw comb**
    - **Eggs and healthy larvae** in existing wax frames
    - Drones

    It's fun to find the queen but you don't need to see her if you see eggs.

2. *Few possible reasons your colony is cranky.*

    - It's **cloudy, windy and/or rain** is incoming.
    - You shook and made noise opening the hive. Try to sneak into it quietly!
    - Your bees are **hungry.**
    - Your bees are **out of room;** give them another super.
    - Your bees are **without a queen.**

- **Another animal** is inside the hive, such as a mouse.
- Bees are hot and **need more ventilation.**

3. *If your bees are aggressive.*

- **Are you wearing dark clothes?** Bees consider black threatening.
- **Did you have a banana before making a hive inspection?** The smell of a banana to a bee is similar to the attack pheromone.
- **Don't wear perfume, hair products and heavy makeup.** Bees will respond to some of the pheromones in those products. Who knows what messages we are giving off by wearing them!

4. *How long should you stay in your hive(s)?*

- Get **in and out as quickly as you can.** In general, no more than 10 minutes per hive.
- I use two muslin kitchen towels I toss over the frames to keep bees calm.
- As I inspect each frame, **I move the towel back** to expose the next frame and cover up the previous frame with the first kitchen towel.

5. *What if I'm scared to death to open my hives?*

Buckle up and take it slow. The bottom line is you are going to have to get comfortable opening your hives.

- The best way to get comfortable is to **repeatedly do it.**
- **Buddy up with another new beekeeper** so you will have more opportunities to get used to opening a hive.
- **Wear your beekeeping suit.**
- **Light up your smoker** and have it handy in case bees get agitated.
- If you **see bees looking back at you,** close up the hive. They are getting ready to say in their own inimitable way you are not welcome. (Yes, that means they are getting ready to sting.)

6. *How frequently should I **check** my hives?*

You should visually check your hives daily or every other day, observing bee behavior and comparing similarities and differences.

- You want to see **bees flying in and out;**

- a **lid top solidly on the hive** and

- **no hive movement** from day to day. You are checking that the hives have not been disturbed.

7. *How frequently should I **inspect** my hives?*

   A reminder: a hive inspection involves you opening up your hives and checking for signs of the queen laying.

   - When you're starting, inspect your hives, in general, **once a month.**

   - **During the nectar flow**, you may need to inspect every **7 to 10 days.**

   - **Use the inspection guide** to make an assessment of your colony and take notes.

   - **Save your weak hive for last**, that's where you may have to spend your most time.

8. *My bees are so gentle, do I really need to wear a suit?*

   I suggest you get used to putting on your safety equipment every time you go out into your apiary.

   Your bees may be gentle for weeks and then one day a guard bee will take her job very seriously and sting you. **Wear your bee suit!**

9. *Do I always have to light my smoker?*

   When you are starting to keep bees, it's good practice to have your working smoker handy at all times.

   - Knowing how to light a smoker **takes practice** so this is a good year to learn.

   - Your colonies will be **bigger next year**; you may need the smoke.

   - **Learn now** so that **when you need it, you will have it.**

10. *Should I always take my hive tool with me?* YES.

    - Get into the habit of **working your hive WITH your hive tool in your hand**, it will help you be quicker when you are in the hive.

    - The hive tool will come in **handy to remove stings.**

    - **Clean your hive tool** in between hive inspections. Ok, so most people won't do this but —

- Definitely **clean your hive tool when you visit another apiary,** both going and coming back. Use alcohol or leave hive tool in your smoker for a few minutes. Let it cool before using again.

11. *What if I can't find the queen?*

    - Look for signs of **freshly laid eggs in royal jelly.**
    - If you see eggs, you know the queen has been in the hive in **the last 3 days.**
    - Gently return the frames and close up the hive. If you see larvae, you know the queen has been in the hive during the last week.
    - Consider buying queens that are marked.

12. *What if a colony is not growing?*

    - One sign of a new colony not growing is lack of food.
    - **Start supplemental feeding** to keep the colony alive and
    - **Consider moving your hives** to a better food source area.

13. *What if bees are hanging around the inner cover hole?*

    Sounds like your bees need room.

    - Check that bees have **easy access** to the rest of the hive.
    - If bees have filled inside frames and are **working the two outer frames**, add a box with frames.

14. *When do I add supers?*

    When worker bees have filled out all of the inside frames and have started working on the last two outer frames. Also check inside frames to make sure queen still has room to lay.

    - If you add too early, you **may not have enough bees** to patrol the new space.
    - If you add too late, bees may have **started to make plans to swarm** because they are out of room.

15. *How do I know when my bees are planning to swarm?*

    Lift your hive boxes and check the bottom of the frames for peanut-shaped cells. See page 109 for photo. Those are swarm cells. The colony may be raising queens in preparation to swarm.

Look inside the peanut-shaped cell. **If you see royal jelly in the swarm cell,** the colony is growing a new queen to swarm.

- **Monitor the swarm cell.** Once the swarm cell is capped, the colony may swarm any day.

- You can **move that swarm cell** with a frame of brood from another colony with a frame of beebread and honey to a nuc to raise a new bee colony.

16. *How can I tell if a swarm queen has hatched, or eclosed?*

   Look for a peanut-looking queen cell.

Swarm cells look like ***peanuts*** *hanging from usually the bottom of the frame. A colony may swarm any time after the swarm cell (s) is/are capped. Bees will fill a queen cell with white royal jelly as they start to raise a queen bee.*

- You will find swarm queen cells most often on the bottom of a frame. A swarm queen cell that has eclosed will have the **hinged tip open,** a sign that a new queen bee has emerged.

- If you had other queen cells, **the first queen to emerge will kill the rest of the queens** still in their cells.

- If you see **a queen cell torn from the side,** that is a sign another queen bee has destroyed the developing queen still in her cell.

17. *When can I harvest honey?*

- You can harvest honey when your bees have first saved **50-80 pounds of honey** needed for winter food. **In first year with you**, your honey bees will spend most of their energy **making wax comb and storing nectar.**

- If you are **feeding your bees sugar syrup,** you should **not harvest their stores,** you will be harvesting dehydrated sugar syrup. Sugar syrup is not honey.

18. *How do I know if my colony is being robbed?*

Cleaning/leaving honey frames in the open and/or hives opened too long may entice robbing. Weak and queenless colonies may also get robbed.

Watch hive entrance. Robber bees will fly straight in; guard bees will wrestle intruders and torn wax will be on bottom board.

To prevent robbing, install entrance robber screens and mesh cages. Also cover exposed hive with damp sheet leaving an exit for resident bees. Monitor.

19. *When adding a honey super, do I **just sit it on top of the hive?***

If this is your second box - either medium or deep - over your first and only box, this will become part of the brood chamber and give your queen more room to lay. Usually the brood is not disturbed by moving frames. If you are adding a second or more honey super, you will add the newest honey super box over the brood box and move the other honey supers on top of this new honey box. This **bottom supering** allows the colony to have closer and quicker access to the new space in the newest added super.

*Young bees will take orientation flights and will be doing **"figure eights"** in front of the hive.*

HIVE INSPECTION GUIDE

Date _____ Time _____ Hive ID _____

Inspection Purpose _____

WEATHER CONDITIONS

Temperature _____

Wind Speed _____

Precipitation _____

FORAGING SIGNS

☐ Pollen

☐ Nectar

WHAT'S BLOOMING?

_____

_____

_____

_____

_____

_____

HIVE HEALTH

☐ Good Temper

☐ Bad Temper

☐ Small hive beetles

☐ Wax moths

☐ Nosema streaks

☐ *Varroa* signs

☐ Swarm cells

☐ Supersedure cells

QUEEN STATUS

☐ Saw Queen

☐ Marked Queen

COLONY STATUS

☐ Weak

☐ Moderate

☐ Strong

FRAME NUMBERS

_____Brood Frames

_____Bee Bread Frames

_____ Drone Frames

_____ Honey Frames

_____ Open Comb

BOX NUMBERS

____ All Medium Boxes

_____ Deep Brood Box

_____Medium Box

____ Horizontal Frames

FEEDING

☐ Pollen substitute

☐ Sugar water ratio____

☐ Honey frames

☐ Sugar cakes

☐ Other: _____

GOOD TO KNOW
TIP

*Watch for **spider webs near hives**; spiders will capture and save bees in webs. If you find pieces of bee bodies on hive tops, migrating birds snack on bees including **Purple Martins** and **Summer Tanagers.** Summer Tanagers are tomato red and are known as the "bee eaters."*

Your Notes

_____

_____

_____

_____

_____

_____

_____

_____

_____

CHAPTER 10

Honey

HOW SWEET IT IS!

Out of 20,000 bees worldwide, **only four bee species** produce honey of any significance to humans including honey bees.

Honey is also the only food that includes all the substances necessary to sustain life, including water.

- Honey is **twice as sweet as sugar.** One honey teaspoon has 64 calories.
- US Department of Agriculture Grade A honey is 18.6% water content.
- **Honey is a liquid carbohydrate.** It consists of glucose and fructose in water with other sugars, acids, minerals and proteins dehydrated by honey bees to 16-18%. Honey with higher water content can ferment.
- Honey is not sugar syrup. Sugar syrup is not honey.
- **Honey crystallizes at 65-70°F** depending on the source of nectar. Some honeys crystallize faster than others.

Honey dippers make serving liquid honey easier. Well, at least less messy. Twirl the wooden honey dipper in honey so the honey can easily be transferred without dripping.

TYPES OF HONEY

- **Raw Strained Honey:** Liquid honey removed from comb.
- **Cut Comb or Comb Honey:** Cut wax comb with honey from a tree, frame or other support structures.

Comb honey is the most expensive honey available. The wax with honey is spread on toast or bread.

- **Chunk Honey:** Well-trimmed honeycomb in a jar surrounded by liquid honey.
- **Creamed (Whipped) Honey:** Liquid honey seeded with a starter and exposed to cold temperature to crystallize the honey into a smooth, butter-like consistency.
- **Mono Floral Honey:** a type of honey which has a distinct flavor or other attribute due to its being predominantly from the nectar of one plant species. Does not provide bees with all of the vitamins, minerals and amino acids bees need to remain healthy.
- **Multi Floral Honey:** often called "wildflower" honey, it is honey from a wide range of flowers as opposed to single source or mono floral honey.

HONEY APPLICATION

Honey has **antimicrobial properties that delay spoilage**, making it handy in baked goods.

Honey is also used in some medical procedures because it **discourages the growth of yeasts and spore-forming bacteria.**

MEDICINAL HONEY USES

According to Dr. Kirsten Traynor, honey has long been established in the medical community to help with **coughs and wound healing** including:

- **Abscesses**
- **Burns and scalds**
- **Leg lacerations**
- **Surgical wounds/infections**
- **Traumatic wounds**

Beware of making, and believing, other claims. There are other medically approved uses. Check first with a medical practitioner.

As beekeepers, **we should not be making medicinal claims** and giving medical advice unless we are also a certified medical practitioner.

Do you see how bees are building up wax cells on the frame? They started at the frame top and are working their way down. **This is new wax-covered plastic foundation in a medium wooden frame.**

FREQUENTLY ASKED QUESTIONS ABOUT HONEY

WHEN CAN I EXTRACT HONEY?

That depends on how strong a colony is, how well the plants are generating nectar, and the storage space a colony has. **It may take a couple of years** before your bees produce more than the 50-80 lbs of honey each colony needs to make it through winter.

WHAT IS A HONEY STOMACH?

Worker bees have two stomachs, one for nourishment and the second to store nectar. The honey stomach is a crop that dispenses enzymes that mix in with collected nectar and honeydew. It also allows nectar to be regurgitated.

WHEN DO I ADD/REMOVE QUEEN EXCLUDER?

Queen excluders are used to temporarily prevent the queen bee from laying in honey supers. You don't want to keep queen excluders on too long or in winter. Bees will move through queen excluder in winter but queen won't be able to move with them.

WHAT IS HONEY TO BEES?

Honey is a bee's version of winter canning. Bees produce honey as food stores for the colony during long winter months. They consume honey when flowers aren't blooming and little or no nectar is available to them in nature.

WHAT HAS MORE VALUE—HONEY OR WAX?

As a beekeeper, your colonies need wax for storage of eggs, beebread, pollen and honey. Your bees need honey for winter food so **both have value.**

- It takes bees the equivalent of **two frames of honey to make one wax frame.** As you establish your first honey bee colonies, your honey bees will spend their first year making wax on your new frames as well as storing honey.

- By your second year, bees **will have a head start with frames of wax they**

made in their first year. If conditions are favorable, they should be able to use their energy to store honey for winter as well as making extra honey.

- A 30,000 bee colony will make more honey than two smaller colonies because they will have more foragers bringing in nectar.

CAN ONE EXTRACT IF FEEDING BEES SUGAR SYRUP?

No, sugar syrup is not flower nectar. Sugar syrup does not contain the additional sugars, acids, minerals and proteins in bee-produced honey dehydrated from flower nectar.

CAN I MANAGE BEES TO COLLECT "ORGANIC" HONEY?

US Department of Agriculture has strict production and labeling requirements before a product can be labelled "organic." In addition, for a beekeeper to qualify as "organic," the beekeeper has to certify that all forage within 5 square miles of the hives have not been treated. They also have to ensure nothing has drifted from neighboring fields. For more **info on organic certification: bit.ly/Organic-Labeling**

HOW DO I KNOW THERE IS A GOOD NECTAR FLOW?

Nectar will be raining out of the frames when you tilt them.

HONEY EXTRACTING

There are a number of hand and motorized extractors on the market. **You probably don't need one unless you plan to extract from more than 2-4 hives.**

My bee buddy David straining honey out of the extractor. **Line your extracting space with plastic;** *honey is sticky!*

HAND-EXTRACTING HONEY

If you want to extract a couple of frames of extra honey, you can easily do so by:

- **Work in a warm room** so the honey is liquified:
- **Heat bread knife in water**; use heated knife to remove wax caps.
- Let **honey drip into a cake sheet** or scrape the comb into a strainer in a bowl;
- Let **honey drip through the strainer overnight** in a warm room.
- **Re-strain honey into bottles.** Allow to settle. Spoon white wax froth off top before sealing.
- Place **remaining empty comb inside hives** for bees to clean up. Don't leave out in the open, it may encourage robbing.

MACHINE EXTRACTORS

Honey extractors use **centrifugal force** to remove honey from beehive frames without damaging them. Then the used wax frames can be returned and re-used in the hives.

Honey extractors are manual or electric.

ADVANTAGES OF MANUAL HONEY EXTRACTORS

- Can be used to extract honey **even where there is no source of electricity.**
- It ensures that delicate wax combs are not damaged because the spinning speed can be controlled by the hands easily.
- Doesn't contribute to your electric bill.
- Less expensive than the electric extractor.

ADVANTAGES OF MOTORIZED HONEY EXTRACTORS

- Electric honey extractors can be **used to extract large amounts in a much quicker time.**
- They are easy to operate. Simply turn on the electric motor and the spinning starts automatically. Should be monitored so that spinning isn't too fast and blows out the wax in frames.
- They are faster compared to manual extractors.
- Can be used by large commercial honey extracting companies.

TWO BASIC TYPES OF MOTORIZED HONEY EXTRACTORS

Here's an easy way to distinguish between the two. **A radial extractor** in the photo, is like the spokes of a wheel with the frame edges facing outward. When the frames are spun, honey is quickly removed from both sides.

A tangential extractor has the foundation facing outwards. To extract honey from both sides, the frames have to be turned once so that the honey will be spun out of both frame sides.

Radial extractors tend to be more expensive than tangential extractors but save time in the long run.

BASIC HONEY EXTRACTING

The biggest challenge in extracting honey is getting the frames off your hives without bees. After gently removing bees off frames, store them in clear containers such as plastic totes to keep bees from getting to them.

- **Extract within 48 hours** of removing frames or
- **Freeze frames for 48-72 hours** to kill any small hive beetle larvae before storing until extracted.

Set up extractor in an area bees can't access such as a plastic, floor-covered CLOSED garage door. Temperature should be at least 80°F to keep honey easily liquefied for easy extraction.

Cut off wax caps. Either use bread knife heated in hot water or a heated knife.

Place frames in extractor.

Crank or start extractor motor and spin until honey is removed from frames.

Place empty frames back in supers.

Place supers full of empty frames inside on top of hives so bees can clean them. **Do not set frames out in open** to open feed or you may encourage robbing.

Transfer honey out of extractor into decanting tank. **Let stand for 24-48 hours.**

Pour through sieve to remove any debris.

Bottle. **Let sit for 2-4 days.** Remove white foam on top before sealing.

Collect wax cappings. Pour honey collected at the bottom of the bucket. Store wax cappings until they can be rendered.

Clean extractor and other equipment before storing.

HOW TO CLEAN EXTRACTED FRAMES

Bees will clean out the frames if you return them to hives. **Don't leave wet frames out in the open;** place them on supers on hives and let the bees access the frames from inside the hive.

Check back in a few days. Bees will have cleaned out the frames.

Gently move bees off the frames and remove frames; then store them.

HOW TO RENDER WAX CAPPINGS

Pick up a soup pan, wooden spoon and sieve at your local thrift store. Used crock pots are also becoming increasingly popular to render, or melt down, wax. Cheesecloth is also useful but optional. Once these are used for wax rendering, you **won't be able use these for anything else.**

Place wax into pan and fill with water until 3 inches from the pot top. You can also place in a crock pot with water.

Gently heat to boiling while slowly stirring wax. **Be careful, wax is flammable!**
- If you have a fire, don't use water to put it out, it will spread the fire.
- Keep a fire extinguisher handy. If you don't have one, **use baking soda and sand to extinguish the flames.**

Once melted, **pour wax into a sieve over a 5-gallon bucket** half full of water.
- **Let wax cool.**
- **Remove the disk of wax** that forms on top of water. Scrape off debris on the bottom of the wax disk while wax disk is still warm.
- **Repeat** to increase wax purity.

To collect more debris, **line sieve with cheesecloth** before pouring melted wax.

Allow wax-covered cheesecloth to dry. **Cut up into small pieces** to use as smoker fire starters.

Store wax disks. Re-melt. Pour into different forms as necessary.

COOKING WITH HONEY

Substitute honey in recipes calling for **molasses and maple syrup.**

In general, **honey can be substituted for sugar** in most baked goods but there will be a change in texture.

To **use honey in place of 1 cup sugar:**
- Use ½ to ⅓ cup of honey. Add ¼ teaspoon of baking soda for every cup of honey in recipe.
- Reduce another liquid in recipe by ¼ cup per cup of honey used, and
- Reduce oven temperature by 25°F.

A friend who does a lot of baking says honey can be substituted for sweetener without these changes. Try both ways and see what works for you!

LABELING HONEY FOR SALE

Check with your state laws on labeling requirements, those can vary.

LABELING HONEY FOR SALE IN MISSOURI

In 2015, the Missouri Legislature **changed Missouri's honey labeling laws** eliminating the requirement for bottling in a commercial kitchen.

Missouri Revised Statues 261.241 (2015) specifies beekeepers selling honey
- "whose annual sales of honey are **fifty thousand dollars or less per domicile** shall not be required to construct or maintain separate facilities for the bottling of honey.
- **Such sellers shall be exempt** from all remaining health standards and regulations for the bottling of honey pursuant to sections 196.190 to 196.271 **if**

they meet the following requirements:

- **Honey shall be bottled in the domicile of the person harvesting and selling the honey;**
- **Honey shall be labeled** with the following information in legible English as set forth in subsection 2 of this section;
- **Annual gross sales shall not exceed fifty thousand dollars.** The person harvesting such honey shall maintain a record of sales of honey bottled and sold. The record shall be available to the regulatory authority when requested."

*My honey samples meeting **Missouri's 2015** honey labeling requirements.*

MISSOURI HONEY LABELING

The honey shall be labeled with the following information:

- **Name and address of the persons preparing the food;**
- **Common name of the food; and**
- **The name of all ingredients in the food.**

Sellers of honey who violate the provisions of this section may be enjoined from selling honey by the Department of Health and Senior Services."

Honey labeled as **"organic" has to be certified by US Department of Agriculture.** In general, businesses directly involved in food production can be certified, including seed suppliers, farmers, food processors, retailers and restaurants. The "organic" and "certified organic" labels cannot legally be used without formal certification.

BASIC HONEY MEASUREMENT

Honey in the US is typically measured and sold in **net weight ounces: NET WT. OZ.** 1 lb. 6 oz. (22 ounces).

Net weight ounces refer to the mass, or weight, of a product. To get an accurate number, weight the container with lid first; add the honey; then subtract the container with lid weight to get an accurate number.

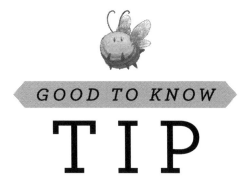

GOOD TO KNOW

TIP

HOW TO MAKE CREAMED HONEY

Whatever you call it—whipped honey, spun honey, I call it creamed honey—is NOT hard to do and they make great gifts. There are a few initial steps that make this a success:

1. **You will need an area that is not heated to store the seeded honey** in jars to set. I have used both an unheated storage area and my garage, both successfully. Ideal temperature is around 50°F to 57°F.

2. **You will also need a seed starter.** There are several options on the market from a dry powder option to actual creamed honey. I have only used actual creamed honey and started with one I found at a grocery store. Once I had mine, however, I didn't have to buy any more. I use mine as my starter for my next batches.

3. **You will need the containers** you want to pour the seeded honey in. There is no middle step in this process, no weeks in between when you make the creamed honey and when you bottle it. The raw honey is mixed with the seed, then it is poured into the final containers to set. If you are planning to make this for gifts, then collect the containers you plan to use and have them clean, on hand, and ready to be filled.

A friend shared some creamed honey with me.
*This little jar had a **delightful surprise inside!***

Ingredients

- *Creamed honey starter*
- *Honey*
- *Jars with lids and labels*

The basic ratio is one part creamed honey to 10 parts raw strained honey. Select a wonderful seeded honey to start because the raw strained honey will copy those crystals.

Pour the room temperature raw honey in a bowl; add the room temperature seeded honey, then slowly mix it. When I started, I would carefully mix by hand, which is fine for small quantities. Don't use a beater; you will end up with bubbles.

Pour into containers. Add lids. I lined a cardboard box with plastic bags to protect the cardboard, added the containers, then stored the box in a cool area to set.

2 oz. containers set within a day. Larger 6 oz. containers set within a couple of days. Larger containers will take longer to be ready. In general, it should take a week to 10 days for the honey to fully set.

If you don't like how they turned out, place the mixture in a glass jar in a pan of hot water off the heat source. Let it melt back to liquified honey.

Store creamed honey in a cool area, not close to heat such as the stove or in a window. For most people, it doesn't last long so they don't have to worry about storage!

Your Notes

_____

_____

_____

_____

_____

_____

_____

_____

_____

Your Notes

CHAPTER 11

First Year Beekeeping Calendar

"The only time I ever believed that I knew all there was to know about beekeeping was the first year I was keeping them. Every year since I've known less and less and have accepted the humbling truth that bees know more about making honey than I do."

Sue Hubbell, *A Book of Bees: And How to Keep Them*

MIDWEST BEEKEEPER'S TYPICAL FIRST YEAR & WHAT YOUR BEES ARE DOING

This should give you an idea of what honey bees living in the Midwest **are doing in managed hives through a typical year.**

I included examples of when to monitor for *Varroa* mites and when to apply oxalic acid vapor. Develop your own *Varroa* management plan and follow product directions.

FIRST YEAR BEEKEEPING GOAL

Your goal this first year of keeping bees is to help your bees through their first winter with you. **Once they have pulled through, you get to call yourself "a beekeeper!"**

JANUARY

> BEEKEEPER

Find a local bee club and start attending club meetings. Listen. Ask questions.

- ☐ Attend beginning beekeeping classes.
- ☐ Order beekeeping and hive equipment.
- ☐ Order bees. If you are ordering a nuc, most nucs are raised in deep nuc boxes. If you want a nuc for a medium frame sized hive, ask if they are available with medium frames. Ask whether colonies will be treated for *Varroa* mites and what kind of treatment they will get.

> BEES

Bees surround the queen in a cluster, shaking their wing muscles to keep themselves warm.

Worker bees rotate through the cluster to stay warm. Small hive beetles winter over inside the cluster.

When temperatures are over 45°F, bees will take cleansing flights and drag dead bee bodies out of the hive.

Queen may start laying eggs. If bees have to decide between keeping brood warm or moving to eat, they will die keeping the brood warm.

Bees will consume 25-30 pounds of stored honey, more this month if the weather is warm.

FEBRUARY

> BEEKEEPER

Have you shopped for hive equipment yet?

- ☐ If you make your own hives, order pre-cut wood, then glue first, and nail/screw together.
- ☐ Paint on warm days; it can take longer to dry in cold weather.

BEES ▸

Queen continues to lay.

On warm days, bees will be busy taking out dead bodies, taking cleansing flights and looking for pollen.

This is the month when colonies may run out of food and die of starvation. Large colonies may also die if they haven't been managed for *varroa*.

Bees will consume 25 pounds of stored honey this month.

MARCH

BEEKEEPER ▸

Have bee suit in hand?

- ☐ Volunteer to go visit a hive with a practicing beekeeper on a warm day.
- ☐ Start observing what trees, shrubs and flowers are blooming within a 2-mile radius of your planned hive location.
- ☐ Continue to read beekeeping books.

BEES ▸

Queen continues to lay. Bees start bringing in early pollen for baby food.

APRIL

BEEKEEPER ▸

You should be ready for your bees:

- ☐ Hives in hand and/or finished.
- ☐ Hive locations scouted and prepared.
- ☐ Plan finished for what trees, shrubs and flowers will be planted after danger of last frost.

BEES ▸

As weather warms, bees find more pollen sources; usually month when drones first appear.

MAY

BEEKEEPER

Depending on weather, you may be getting your packages, nucs or colonies this month.

☐ The bee provider should notify you of a good delivery and/or pick up date.

☐ Spring nectar flow begins, when bees will quickly grow in population.

☐ If you have your bees, check bottom of frames for queen swarm cells.

BEES

The colony is quickly growing.

When temperatures range from 74°F to 86°F the nectar flow is on.

Worker bees are pulling wax and collecting nectar.

JUNE

BEEKEEPER

Your bees are in their new location and getting oriented.

☐ Place a seat close by so you can observe them as they fly in and out.

☐ If you don't have plants to feed them, you will need to feed them sugar syrup and pollen patties.

☐ Check colonies every 7-10 days to make sure bees have enough hive space.

BEES

Bees are extremely busy. As they run out of space they start building swarm cells at the bottom of frames.

More nectar and pollen is getting stored.

JULY

BEEKEEPER

Check colonies weekly to make sure they have space to store honey, pollen and eggs.

- ☐ When bees are working the two outside frames, it's time to add a box for more room.
- ☐ Monitor for stored food; remember each colony needs the equivalent of one medium super full of stored honey for winter. Monitor *Varroa* mite levels; do a sugar shake and/or alcohol wash.

  - Nectar flow ends.

BEES

If weather is hot, bees may hang out outside the hive.

Queen laying may slow down this month as nectar flow ends.

AUGUST

BEEKEEPER

This is the month to be vigilant!

- ☐ Check colony's honey reserves.
- ☐ Feed to stimulate wax glands to produce comb, if needed, to prepare space for fall flow storage.
- ☐ Check for robbing.
- ☐ Drones may be kicked out of hives if food is short.

BEES

Colony's numbers are at their highest this month.

Queen laying slows down or stops.

Bees may consume larvae and stored honey if food sources are scarce.

SEPTEMBER

BEEKEEPER

Get ready for winter.

- ☐ Equalize your colonies with stored honey.
- ☐ Watch for signs of queen-laying and robbing.
- ☐ Apply *Varroa* mite treatment, if appropriate and weather permits. Read mite treatment directions!
- ☐ Look for fall flow from asters and goldenrod to bring in winter stores. If significant stores are not brought in by the latter part of the month, feed heavily 2:1 ration until colony is brought up to weight.

BEES

Winter bees are hatching, these are the ones that will carry the colony through the next 6 months.

Queen laying is slowing or stopping.

Drones may be kicked out.

OCTOBER

BEEKEEPER

Time to tuck hives in for winter.

- ☐ Reduce hive bodies to one deep and one medium honey super or three mediums for winter.
- ☐ Wrap insulation around hives.
- ☐ Set up wind break.
- ☐ Install entrance reducers and/or mouse guards.
- ☐ Add supplemental sugar cakes and perhaps winter pollen patties, as needed and appropriate.

> **BEES**

Worker bees chase and sting drones out of the hive.

Queen laying continues on the decline or has stopped.

NOVEMBER

> **BEEKEEPER**

Inventory your equipment:

- ☐ Store extra hive equipment.
- ☐ Make necessary repairs.
- ☐ Order additional equipment for next year.
- ☐ Consider applying oxalic acid vapor or dribble for *Varroa* mites two weeks after last hard frost when colony is broodless.

> **BEES**

As cold weather moves in, bees will form a cluster with the queen inside to keep warm.

DECEMBER

> **BEEKEEPER**

Read a good book. Enjoy the holidays.

- ☐ Look forward to a full year of beekeeping next year.
- ☐ Monitor and check your hives but don't inspect (and break propolis seals)!

> **BEES**

Bees are inside hives clustered for warmth.

Queen may not be laying at this time, leaving the colony without brood.

Worker bees will take cleansing flights during warm days.

They are consuming honey.

GOOD TO KNOW
TIP

*Place supplemental sugar cakes **over the cluster** so bees can easily access it during cold winter temperatures. **Locate the cluster by placing your hand** under the inner cover and finding the heat source. In this colony, I found the cluster had moved away from under the supplemental sugar cakes. I moved the sugar cakes to sit once again over the cluster.*

FIRST YEAR BEEKEEPING CHECK LIST

Your goal: **help your bees through their first winter with you. Once they have pulled through,** you get to call yourself **"a beekeeper!"**

JANUARY

☐ Find a local bee club and start attending club meetings. Listen. Ask questions.

☐ Attend beginning beekeeping classes.

☐ Order beekeeping and hive equipment.

☐ Order package bees.

☐ If you are ordering nucs, most nucs are raised in deep nuc boxes. If you want a nuc for a medium frame sized hive, ask if they are available with medium frames. Ask what, if any, *Varroa* treatment the colonies will get.

☐ If you are getting full hives, make sure to order the right size frames for your desired hive equipment. You may need to provide your bee supplier with frames in exchange for the ones being sold to you.

☐ Plan your spring and fall plantings.

☐ Other: _____

FEBRUARY

☐ Buy beekeeping equipment.

☐ Buy hives.

☐ If you make your own hives, order pre-cut wood, then glue first, and nail/screw together.

☐ Paint on warm days; it can take longer to dry in cold weather.

☐ Other: _____

☐ _____

MARCH

☐ Bee suit and equipment ordered and on hand.

☐ Volunteer to visit a hive with a practicing beekeeper on a warm day.

☐ Start observing what trees, shrubs and flowers are blooming within a 2-mile radius of your planned hive location.

☐ Continue to read beekeeping books.

☐ Other:

☐ _____

☐ _____

APRIL

☐ Hives in hand and/or finished.

☐ All other basic beekeeping equipment is in hand.

☐ Plan finished for what trees, shrubs and flowers will be planted after danger of last frost.

☐ Other: _____

☐ _____

MAY

☐ Bee provider notified you of a good bee delivery date.

☐ If you have bees, check frame bottoms for queen swarm cells.

☐ Swarm season begins Mother's Day weekend where I live in Missouri. Ask around, when does swarming start where you live?

☐ Other: _____

☐ _____

JUNE

- ☐ Your bees are in their new home and getting oriented.
- ☐ Sitting bench is close by so you can observe bees as they move around their new home.
- ☐ If you don't have plants to feed them during nectar flow, feed sugar syrup and pollen patties to get them established.
- ☐ Check colonies every 7-10 days to make sure bees have enough hive space.
- ☐ Other: _____
- ☐ _____
- ☐ _____

JULY

- ☐ Weekly check colonies to make sure they have space.
- ☐ Monitor for stored food; remember each colony needs the equivalent of one medium super full of stored honey for winter.
- ☐ Nectar flow ends.
- ☐ Watch for robbing.
- ☐ Check for *Varroa* mite count with sugar shake or alcohol wash.
- ☐ Other: _____
- ☐ _____
- ☐ _____

*Small hive beetle (SHB) numbers increase during summer. Use **plastic condiment bottles,** one with mineral oil, the other with homemade lure, to easily refill SHB traps.*

AUGUST

- ☐ Check colony's honey reserves.
- ☐ Feed to stimulate wax glands to produce wax comb, if needed, to prepare space for fall flow storage.
- ☐ Check for robbing and *Varroa* mite levels.
- ☐ Drones may be kicked out of the hives if food supplies are low.
- ☐ Other: _____
- ☐ _____
- ☐ _____

SEPTEMBER

- ☐ Equalize colonies with stored honey.
- ☐ Watch for signs of queen-laying and robbing.
- ☐ Apply *Varroa* mite treatment, if appropriate and weather permits. Read mite treatment directions!
- ☐ Look for fall flow from asters and goldenrod to bring in winter stores. If significant stores are not brought in by the latter part of month, feed heavily 2:1 sugar syrup until colony is brought up to weight.
- ☐ Do not try to save drones kicked out of the hives; bees will grow new ones next spring.
- ☐ Plant trees and shrubs.
- ☐ Other: _____
- ☐ _____
- ☐ _____

OCTOBER

- ☐ Reduce hive bodies to one deep and one medium honey super or three mediums for winter.
- ☐ Wrap insulation around hives for wind breaks.
- ☐ Set up wind breaks.
- ☐ Install mouse guards.
- ☐ Add supplemental sugar cakes, as appropriate.
- ☐ Check *Varroa* mite count.
- ☐ Other: _____
- ☐ _____
- ☐ _____

NOVEMBER

- ☐ Option: oxalic acid vapor or dribble treatment two weeks after the last hard frost for *Varroa* management.
- ☐ Store extra hive equipment
- ☐ Make necessary equipment repairs.
- ☐ Order additional equipment for next year.
- ☐ Plant trees and shrubs.
- ☐ Other: _____
- ☐ _____
- ☐ _____

DECEMBER

☐ Monitor and check your hives but don't inspect (and break propolis seals)!

☐ Add supplemental sugar cakes and pollen patties, as needed.

☐ Read a good book. Enjoy the holidays!

☐ Look ahead to a full year of beekeeping next year!

☐ Other: _____

☐ _____

☐ _____

GOOD TO KNOW

TIP

*Ralph and Luella Gamber came up with the idea for **a honey bear container** in 1957. It was inspired by Winnie the Pooh. Today the honey bear is still recognized as the quintessential US honey container.*

Your Notes

Your Notes

CHAPTER 12

Second Year Beekeeping Calendar

"I like pulling on a baggy bee suit, forgetting myself and getting as close to the bees' lives as they will let me, remembering in the process that there is more to life than the merely human."

Sue Hubbell, *A Book of Bees: And How to Keep Them*

A BEEKEEPER'S SECOND YEAR

Your second year keeping bees will be different than your first. Although honey bees are in general following their schedule, yours will be more work since you now have had bees through a whole year instead of just six months.

In general, **this is the year when you will learn new techniques for managing your bees.**

Remember **no two years** of beekeeping **are ever the same!**

SECOND YEAR BEEKEEPING GOALS & REMINDERS

- **Keep detailed notes** in your diary along the way such as when you got bees; when you tested for *Varroa*; when you re-queened, split and added brood.
- **Take pictures;** save and date them so you can compare bee progress.

- Note **bee behaviors and ask questions** at club meetings.

- **Develop a bee buddy** so you can share and compare notes.

- When someone **loans you a piece of equipment, return it** and thank them. Then **help someone else** when you can.

- Honey bees can change their plans mid-stream and they won't leave you a memo. Spend time early on observing your colonies and **learning how to "read your bees."**

- A beekeeper needs to **anticipate, and plan,** for the beginning and the end of nectar flows.

- **Wear your beekeeping suit.** Your bees are now vested in their new home and may be more defensive. Colonies will also be larger this year.

- **Remember bees are in charge;** you are landlords and staff. On a good day!

*Laundry bags are handy to cover nucs **when transporting bees.** The laundry bag keeps the bees confined until they arrive at their new location. Very handy to use with that nervous driver.*

SECOND YEAR BEEKEEPING CHECK LIST

Develop your plan for the year. Your goal is to get ahead of your bees so you are prepared and ready to work with them. You should be thinking 6 months ahead of where you are now. (See, time travel does exist!) **What else do you want to add based on your first year of keeping bees?**

JANUARY

- ☐ Check bees for honey. Supplement feed sugar cakes if bees running short of honey. Locate cluster by placing hand under inner cover and finding cluster heat. Place supplemental food over cluster.
- ☐ Do not break hive propolis seals by opening boxes; only peek under inner covers.
- ☐ Shop for basic beekeeping equipment.
- ☐ If planning to expand, start the search for nucs, packages and queen bees.
- ☐ Make necessary hive box repairs. Inventory what you may need for rest of year.
- ☐ Attend local bee club meetings, take classes, attend conferences.
- ☐ Other: _____

FEBRUARY

- ☐ Shop for equipment. Many beekeeping companies have late winter/early spring sales with free shipping. If planning to expand, continue the search for nucs, packages and queen bees.
- ☐ Paint hive bodies and assemble frames/parts. Paint can take 1-3 months to fully dry. Use quality primer and paint.
- ☐ If buying used equipment, ask why they are selling.
- ☐ If using used equipment, thoroughly clean before using. Look for evidence of prior pest damage.
- ☐ During warm week to encourage build up, feed pollen substitute to boost brood laying. (Optional)
- ☐ Attend local bee club meetings, take classes, attend conferences.
- ☐ Other: _____

MARCH

☐ Air out wax frames stored in plastic containers in Para-Moth™ before placing in hive.

☐ Add sticks and rocks to "bee bar" birdbaths to make sure bees have easy access to water within a quarter mile of hives.

☐ Monitor colonies for supplemental food needs; feed as necessary.

☐ Order extra queens if planning to split.

☐ If you want to catch swarms, register on swarm-catching lists.

☐ Prepare for Spring *Varroa* mite treatment and monitor *Varroa* mite levels (sugar shake or alcohol wash.)

☐ Inspect for ants using inner cove as home. Treat with ground/powdered cinnamon.

☐ Make small hive beetle lure and let ferment prior to use.

☐ Get a soil test done of your planting area through your local Extension office so you know what to plant.

☐ Other: _____

APRIL

☐ Inspect colonies. Add small hive beetle traps with lure and monitor *Varroa* mite levels (sugar shake or alcohol wash.)

☐ Pull together swarm-catching equipment.

☐ Prepare nuc(s) 2-5 days before new queens arrive.

☐ Prepare hive bodies before new packages arrive.

☐ Have new boxes with frames ready to add to existing colonies.

☐ Monitor weather for best conditions to split. If you want honey, split after spring nectar flow.

☐ Blooming blackberries mark the beginning of spring nectar flow in Missouri, where I keep bees. What indicates the start of the nectar flow in your area?

_____

☐ Other: _____

MAY

- ☐ Once spring nectar starts, monitor brood boxes to ensure queen has laying space. Add supers when bees are working the outermost frames.
- ☐ Check the bottom of frames for swarm queen cells.
- ☐ If you ordered bees, install packages and pick up bees. Ask if treated for *Varroa*.
- ☐ Monitor small hive beetles and *Varroa* mite levels (sugar shake or alcohol wash.).
- ☐ Respond to swarm calls. Swarm season in Midwest usually begins around Mother's Day in early May.
- ☐ Last hard frost day is May 10; plant annuals.
- ☐ Other: *If using virgin queens, carefully monitor time to mate and begin laying, Weather may impact mating and successful return to hive.*
- ☐ Other: _____

JUNE

- ☐ Check hives weekly; take notes of observations. Take photos and videos for later reference. What are *Varroa* mite levels? Done a sugar shake or alcohol wash to monitor?
- ☐ Add supers as necessary to allow growth and prevent swarming.
- ☐ Bees should be able to find pollen and nectar without supplemental feeding unless spring is late and blooming season has been delayed.
- ☐ If package bees, feed sugar syrup to help get started.
- ☐ Feed swarms. Learn sugar to water ratios for best effect on colonies.
- ☐ Last month to buy perennials and get them in ground before hot weather makes planting difficult.
- ☐ Other: _____

JULY

- ☐ Continue hive observations; make inspections to detect pests and diseases. Monitor *Varroa* mite levels with sugar shake or alcohol wash. Levels should be increasing. What is your plan to manage?
- ☐ Inspect bees regularly for small hive beetles. Kill adult ones; monitor for larvae. Refresh traps.
- ☐ Usually the end of the flower nectar flow.
- ☐ Feed new colonies sugar syrup to help them draw comb.
- ☐ Assess how much nectar each colony has stored so far. If they have more than 50-80 pounds per colony, you can extract honey for yourself.
- ☐ Water plants with underground wand to keep roots hydrated.
- ☐ Other: _____

AUGUST

- ☐ A new colony may not have enough food stored; feed to keep colonies strong and storing winter supplies. Feed inside the hive to reduce robbing.
- ☐ During dearth, new eggs/larvae may not be seen due to bees eating young for protein. Queen may still be laying.
- ☐ Refresh small hive beetle traps.
- ☐ Note if drones are kicked out of the hive; that's a sign of limited hive stores.
- ☐ Monitor for robbing. When temps are over 86°F plants stop producing nectar and pollen.
- ☐ Review *Varroa* management plan and follow directions for winter bees mite treatment..
- ☐ Water trees, plants and shrubs with underground watering wand including established ones. Old trees and shrub roots also need water when temperatures are above 90°F.
- ☐ Other: *Extract during warm temperatures to make the process easier!*
- ☐ Other: _____

SEPTEMBER

- ☐ Prepare hives for winter. Check hives for stored honey. Each colony will need 50-80 pounds of stored honey per hive.
- ☐ Inspect weak colonies for pests and diseases.
- ☐ Unite weak colonies to a medium or strong colony.
- ☐ Monitor for robbing and install robbing screens if necessary.
- ☐ Move refreshed small hive beetle traps to the center of the hive box.
- ☐ Order plants for delivery next spring; pick up spring blooming bulbs for fall planting.
- ☐ Other: _____

OCTOBER

- ☐ Reduce entrances and install mouse guards.
- ☐ Install windbreak in front of hives.
- ☐ Wrap up hives for wind breaks.
- ☐ Bees will kick drones out.
- ☐ Review *Varroa* management plan and adjust for this year and next.
- ☐ Leave flower heads on plants so bees can pick up leftover pollen on warm days.
- ☐ Other: _____

When combining with newspapers, remember to **make small slits in the newspaper** *before adding a second box so the pheromones from the two colonies can more easily combine.*

NOVEMBER

☐ If short of stored honey, add supplemental sugar cakes as needed on top of feeding shims.

☐ Consider oxalic acid vapor or dribble treatment for *Varroa* when hive is without brood, usually two weeks after the last hard frost through the end of the year.

☐ Depending on weather, reduce entrances.

☐ Ensure bees have good ventilation and stay dry. Cold doesn't kill bees, moisture does.

☐ Consider using house insulation to wrap colonies.

☐ Store equipment. Check catalogs for additional hive parts.

☐ Make a list of what plants you want to add next year.

☐ Other: _____

DECEMBER

☐ Ensure rain/snow is not getting into hive.

☐ Check entrance reducers; keep them clean of snow and dead bees so live bees can take cleansing flights.

☐ Open hive inner cover top if temperatures are more than 45°F and sunny and if it is necessary to check existing food supplies.

☐ Do not break hive apart; bees have sealed hive with propolis to make it snug for winter.

☐ Check sugar cakes on top of frames to make sure they are not too dry. Spray with water so bees can access sugar.

☐ Review your diary for what plants you saw your bees visiting earlier in the year. Make plans to plant more next year.

☐ Other: _____

ONGOING QUESTIONS TO PONDER

- What worked well this past year?
- What will you do differently next year?
- What do you want to try and learn next?

*This is a 1½ inches tall homemade feeding shim made with quarter inch hardware cloth. Sugar cakes and pollen patties can **safely sit on top of the hardware cloth** and are easily accessible to bees through winter.*

HOW MANY JOBS DID YOU RECOGNIZE ON THE COVER?

Worker bee jobs represented on the front cover include:

- Foragers
- Guard bees
- House bees
- Nurse bee (only one with a nursing hat)
- Queen retinue
- Water carriers

Others represented on cover:

- Queen Begonia
- Drones (male bees)
- Blackberries in bloom

Enjoy coloring our cover illustration on the next page as a reminder of the different jobs workers bees do in a colony.

Native blackberries in bloom, on the book cover, are a sign in some areas that the nectar flow is starting. "The flow" is when flowers entice pollinators with nectar. Bees collect flower nectar to dehydrate into honey and store for winter food.

Your Notes

_____

_____

_____

_____

_____

_____

_____

_____

_____

CHAPTER 13

Beekeeping Not for You?

Not everyone decides to keep honey bees. But **there are things you can still do** to help honey bees and other pollinators.

The following is a beginning list of ways you can help bees:

HERE'S HOW YOU CAN STILL HELP POLLINATORS, INCLUDING HONEY BEES! *(check all that apply)*	
What you can do	*How and where*
☐ **Set up and make native bee houses**	Hang native bee houses within 100 feet of trees and plants you want pollinated. Store houses in protected area in winter.
☐ Compost	Return kitchen and table scraps to your garden as **compost** to enrich and improve soil.
☐ **Replace Turf Grass with Flowers**	**Plant micro clovers and other micro ground covers that offer pollinator food.** Expand flower beds to plant more flowers. **Plant native trees, shrubs and flowers,** they have ongoing relationship with local pollinators.

☐ **Stop Using Pesticides**	Spray water bottle with dishwashing soap will address many hobby gardener pests. **Learn to companion plant;** use compatible plants to naturally deter bugs. **Don't mix insecticides, pesticides, herbicides.** If you use any of these products, **read and follow label instructions.**
☐ **Plant More Native Trees, Shrubs, Flowers**	Native pollinators depend on native trees, shrubs and flowers for cover and food. **Keep them safe and fed!** Natives will also more quickly and easily get established in your garden.
☐ **Sponsor/ take Missouri Master Pollinator Steward classes**	**Take a pollinator steward class** to get to know pollinators and how to help them: **bit.ly/How-to-start-a-MPS-program**
☐ **Apply to make your garden a Monarch Way Station**	These kinds of programs that certify gardens **provide guidelines** on **how to make your garden pollinator-friendly:** **monarchwatch.org/waystations/certify.html**
☐ **Become a Bee City or a Bee Campus**	**Increase pollinator habitat** working with your local community and campus and be recognized through the Xerxes Society program: **www.beecityusa.org** **www.beecityusa.org/what-is-a-bee-campus.html**

Your Notes

_____

_____

_____

_____

_____

_____

_____

_____

_____

Your Notes

CHAPTER 14

Beekeeper Pledge

Congratulations, you have decided to **become a beekeeper!**

Yes, it's a lot of information at once but if you think of your honey bees as in part dependent on you, you will significantly increase your rate of success in not only keeping honey bees but in keeping them healthy.

To be a good beekeeper, **you agree to do the following:**

1. Be considerate in placing your bees:

Maintain all colonies at least 10 feet away or the minimum distances required from property lines by any local ordinances.

- **Place a 40-foot plus barrier between any colony and any human traffic area** or any animal that is penned or tethered. The barrier should establish bee flyways above head height.

- **Maintain a water source** accessible to your colonies located at least half the distance closer than any water source on property owned by others.

- **Avoid opening or disturbing colonies** when neighbors or the general public are participating in outside activities or using machinery within 150 feet of the apiary.

- **Do not tolerate colonies** exhibiting **excessive defensive behavior.** Such colonies should be requeened and the drone brood destroyed.

- Healthy colonies are valuable and theft in some areas could be a problem. **Consider colony placement out of sight of the general public.**

- **Be a good neighbor** by informing adjoining property owners of the placement of your hives. **Address any concerns they may have.**

2. Keep your bees healthy by:

- **Being wary of used equipment bargains,** especially woodenware. Spores of contagious diseases could still be in the wood.

- **Get bees from a trusted source.** If buying an established colony, inspect it for disease and *Varroa* mite load prior to purchase.

- **Place hives in full sun** or in areas of minimal shade to minimize small hive beetles.

- **Separate your hives as much as you can** from each other so pests and diseases have less chance to drift from one hive to the next.

- **Regularly check your bees,** daily or every few days. By checking I mean make sure lids are still on, there's activity at the hive front, nothing has impacted the hive(s).

- **Keep bees only in well-maintained** Langstroth, top bar or other **hives** designed with removable frames allowing proper inspection and management of the individual combs of the colony.

- **Do not open feed.** That encourages robbing, possible contamination to honey crops and increased opportunities for sharing viruses and other diseases.

3. What if there's trouble?

- **Reduce the entrance** so the remaining bees can better guard against robbing.

- **Research and/or quickly seek help** to identify the problem.

4. Ongoing maintenance:

- **Always do a thorough health check** on any colonies from which you wish to make splits or before combining colonies.

- **Rotate one third of the oldest brood comb** out of the apiary each year.

- Take measures to **reduce drifting and robbing** within your apiary.

- Become **familiar with the diseases and pests** which can affect your bees.

- **Provide regular hive inspections** for disease and strive to maintain strong active colonies by monitoring *Varroa* mite and small hive beetle populations and **taking appropriate action when necessary.**

- Properly treat with a product approved for the specific conditions of concern, following all label instructions, or remove and destroy all diseased and/or pest infested colonies.

- **A diagnosis of American foulbrood should be taken very seriously** as it generally is always fatal to the colony and readily spreads to others. Frames and combs should be burned and remaining woodenware scorched. Keep records of your queens, production and management of the individual hives in your apiary.

5. Immediately Deal With Dying or Dead Colonies.
Quick action is necessary:

- **To reduce robbers** spreading *Varroa* mites and pathogens to your other colonies and those of neighboring beekeepers.

- The **woodenware and comb can also be spared** wax moth and small hive beetle damage. Procrastination will lead to a loss of time and beekeeping resources. Guaranteed.

- **Humanely dispatch any remaining live bees** by shaking/brushing into soapy water.

- **Place frames and combs in a freezer for 24 hours prior to reuse** or storage to kill small hive beetle and wax moth larvae.

6. Keep Learning.
Become engaged with the beekeeping community:

- Join your state association.

- Attend and volunteer at your local bee club meetings. If you don't have a local bee club, start one.

- **Never pass on a chance to work bees with a more experienced beekeeper.** Be observant. Learn from others.

- **Give back and become a mentor.**

- **Above all, keep learning and caring for your bees.**

_____

I have read the above and agree to follow these and other established best management practices to keep my honey bees alive and healthy.

Signed _____ Date _____

*One of the more **charming beekeeping traditions** is one started in Germany, according to Tammy Horn, author of "Bees in America." It represents how intertwined the bees and beekeeper become so that when a beekeeper dies, the bees should be told.*

TELLING THE BEES
by Eugene Field, 1893

Out of the house where the slumberer lay
Grandfather came one summer day;
And under the pleasant orchard trees
He spake this-wise to the murmuring bees;
"The clover-bloom that kissed her feet
And the posie-bed where she used to play
Have honey store, but none so sweet
As ere our little one went away,
O bees, sing soft, and, bees, sing low;
For she is gone who loved you so."

A wonder fell on the listening bees
Under those pleasant orchard trees,
And in their toil that summer day
Ever their murmuring seemed to say;
"Child, child, the grass is cool."
And the posies are waking to hear the song
Of the bird that swings by the shaded pool,
"Waiting for one that tarrieth long."
'Twas so they called to the little one then.
As if to call her back' again.

O gentle bees, I have come to say
That grandfather fell to sleep to-day.
And we know by the smile on grandfather's face.
He has found his dear one's biding place.
So, bees, sing soft, and, bees, sing low.
As over the honey-fields you sweep,
To the trees a-bloom and the flowers a-blow
Sing of grandfather fast asleep;
And ever beneath these orchard trees
Find cheer and shelter, gentle bees.

Your Notes

_____

_____

_____

_____

_____

_____

_____

_____

Your Notes

CHAPTER 15

How to Handle Disagreements

BASIC CONFLICT RESOLUTION

There are many **different techniques, and opinions,** about **how to keep honey bees.** As I mentioned earlier, there are a number of influences why, from experience levels to what you are trying to accomplish managing honey bees, that contribute to so many different answers. In other words, **there are a lot of opportunities for misunderstandings.**

Periodically I hear beekeepers settling their disagreements with "they are your bees, do whatever you want." Although I agree that beekeepers make decisions about how to manage honey bees, being a responsible beekeeper also means taking into account the impact of what you may do, or not do, on other beekeepers, and bees, around you.

*My bee buddy David is an **excellent listener.** It's one of the basic skills helpful to have to discuss different opinions about how to successfully manage honey bees.*

If you find yourself in a situation where you disagree with someone:

1. **Check your attitude.** What have you contributed to the situation? Be honest with yourself.

2. Thank the person for sharing with you and **take a break**. Process what you have heard and why you have issues with what you heard.

3. **Continue the discussion at a better time.** Find a safe neutral place to talk. If you are excitable, choose a time when you can be calm. Make it a private space; you don't want this to be a public spectacle, that can easily add to the misunderstandings and derail some sort of settlement.

4. **Clarify what the issue is,** first in your mind, then in re-stating it calmly to the other person. Before moving on, confirm that you clearly understand the differing issues. You may be surprised how many disagreements get settled at this point.

5. If the disagreement is about how something will get done, **try to meet the other party halfway**. Cooperating and collaborating are options besides disagreeing; keep your alternatives open.

6. **Outline what each of you is willing to do.** Develop an agreement that will satisfy all parties. Compromise will most likely be one option. Compromise is when something is fair even though no one is particularly happy about the outcome.

TYPICAL CONTENTIOUS TOPICS

There are a number of topics that can easily generate discord between beekeepers, such as:

- **Do** *Varroa* **mites really exist?**
- **Differences** in **recommended beekeeping techniques**
- Trying **to make bees do things** versus managing what bees naturally do and
- **Disagreeing** with someone's social media postings.

Let's settle the first one here.

VARROA MITES DO EXIST

Varroa mites do exist throughout North America even though we may not see them in their early life cycle. They and associated viruses are considered the leading bee stressors.

Beekeepers who don't manage for *Varroa* in most cases lose their colonies in their third year.

You will find an April 2018 video I took of *Varroa* mites in drone brood comb here: **https://bit.ly/Varroamites.**

And yes, there are steps beekeepers can take to manage *Varroa*. It's commonly accepted in the scientific community that we currently should not expect to eliminate *Varroa* from our colonies. They can and should be managed.

Every year researchers contribute new information about how best to approach *Varroa* so staying on top of current best practices is important. Changing *Varroa* management landscape can also contribute to misunderstandings.

SETTLING BEEKEEPING TECHNIQUE DIFFERENCES

You are entering beekeeping at a time of great flux. When it comes to recommended beekeeping technique differences, your best bet is to **refer to best management practices** based on scientifically based principles.

If someone **chooses to experiment, that is their choice.** As I said early on, best techniques can vary depending on a number of factors. **Professionally vetted and scientifically based beekeeping based on current research** should quickly help to settle differences in approaches and techniques.

LEARN TO WORK WITH BEES

Sometimes beekeepers approach beekeeping as if they are directing the bees. It's a bit of an adjustment when you first start, especially if you are someone used to taking initiative. Or a dog owner. Dog owners are using to training their pets. They expect their furry canine companions to respond as trained.

Being a beekeeper is more like living with a cat. There is a lot of truth to the saying "dogs have owners, cats have staff." Living with cats myself, I am used to being trained by my cats. Well, maybe spoiling them is more accurate. But it's the same approach if you want to be a good beekeeper. You are working with a living species that has its own way of doing things. **It's our job to learn their ways and work with them. As we like to joke, bees don't read beekeeping books.**

One of the biggest lessons I see bees repeatedly teach their beekeepers is **patience**. Besides staying on their toes and remaining flexible. Just because we have observed bees doing something a certain way, or during a certain time frame, doesn't mean they won't be flexible as well. After all, for them it means their survival. And they have been on this Earth far longer than we have.

The bottom line is, **take your cue from the bees,** not the other way around.

WATCH YOUR SOCIAL MEDIA POSTS

Where do we often get information? These days it is on social media platforms. Because they tend to be one-sided, those posts can often generate arguments and fuel disagreements that don't get quickly resolved.

Instead the tendency is to disparage instead of addressing differences. Different opinions are educational; **contentious exchanges should be stopped** especially when they become personal, such as

- Stalking individuals on their personal pages
- Sending threatening private messages and
- Flaunting their club's involvement to try to leverage a desired result.

These practices are not accepted in most social media platforms and break their own platform use rules. Social media administrators have options to end derailed online discussions and **should be asked to do so.**

These kinds of exchanges don't offer value. In the end, they reflect badly on everyone involved.

WHAT IF YOU DISAGREE IN PERSON
WITH ANOTHER BEEKEEPER

Some of the more interesting discussions I have heard have been between beekeepers with different opinions. However, if the exchange starts to get heated, **take a short time out.**

- **Ask clarifying questions.** Most disagreements begin from a misunderstanding so focus on understanding the specifics first.
- **Take the time to listen before judging.** Sometimes there are nuggets of new information even if in the end you still disagree on a principle.

- **If you determine you don't agree, keep asking questions.** Your questions may lead the other person to rethink their position without being confrontational.
- **Finally, you may agree to disagree.** Keep it cordial. If you attend the same club meetings, you want to be able to say hello. Seeing each other regularly may also open opportunities for further information sharing.

HOW TO RESOLVE ISSUES BETWEEN CLUBS

The beekeeping community has the reputation of being mutually supportive and collaborative. There are exceptions. When issues start to surface, it is **best to address them early**.

- **Be open about the issues** and who is best positioned to address them.
- In general, **subject matter experts may be the best** to address best management practice issues.
- If the disagreement is procedural, first **check your club charter and bylaws**; that is your guide for how your club decided to manage itself. Remind everyone of what was agreed to; discuss implications of changing the original agreement and, if appropriate, develop a plan if you decide adjustments need to be made. Don't let the disagreement fester, that encourages passive aggressive behavior on the part of club members.
- If the issue is something other than beekeeping, **club leaders should quietly address those.** Club members want to focus on beekeeping topics.
- If there are personal issues between club representatives, **a neutral third party** may be helpful to keep discussions focused and identify practical solutions.
- **Take notes on whatever is agreed.** Share the notes with all parties concerned. Keep the lines of communication clear and open.

HOW TO BRIDGE BEEKEEPING ASSOCIATIONS

As a new beekeeper you may want to "give back" by volunteering to help with regional and state associations. Volunteers are the foundation of these volunteer organizations. They are not exempt from conflict and disagreements; if anything, they may have more.

As with many volunteer organizations, most disagreements are **money and bylaws related,** including

- Disregarding their own established procedures;

- Not following standard auditing practices and
- Non-profits "endorsing" or appearing to endorse for profit activities and business entities.

In some instances, the groups will work against each other scheduling events the same day. Or they may compete on who attracts what conference speakers, using disparaging language about the other's event.

Beekeeping groups at this level are in leadership positions. Beekeepers are looking to them for assistance, for opportunities to learn and to work together, and to associate with success. As my mother used to periodically remind us kids, **"learn to play nice."** Energy should be re-routed to:

- Identifying **win-win situations.**
- **Scheduling around**, not in competition, with each other's events and activities.
- Remember people are watching; they decide whether to join an organization based on that organization's success. Most people don't choose to be around negative energy.
- If you can't say something positive in public, **don't say anything at all.**

GOOD TO KNOW

TIP

According to Dr. Kirsten Traynor in "Two Million Blossoms, Discovering the Medicinal Benefits of Honey," honey can prevent hangovers. Just in case the idea of keeping bees, and reading this diary, drives you to drink!!

HOW TO PREVENT HANGOVERS WITH HONEY

1. Before heading out, eat honey on crackers. When drinking alcohol, stick to white wine, gin or vodka and consume fruit juices.

2. When you come home, eat more honey on crackers and take two non-steroidal anti-inflammatory pills.

3. You should wake up without a headache!

Your Notes

_____

_____

_____

_____

_____

_____

_____

_____

_____

Your Notes

_____

_____

_____

_____

_____

_____

_____

_____

_____

CHAPTER 16

Recommended Reading List & More

Consider this homework. Some are books, others are magazines and films. Start getting a flavor of what it is to be a beekeeper.

Keep the list of beekeeping terms handy, you will need it as you get to know beekeeping terminology.

There are other good resources available. These happen to be some of my personal favorites.

They will also come in handy around Christmas and birthdays (hint, hint.)

BOOKS (*Mark off as you read them*)

☐ *Collison, Clarence H., What Do You Know?* Everything You've Ever Wanted to Know About Honey Bees....in an Easy to Use Question and Answer Format. Published 2003. Varroa-related materials are missing and/or need to be updated but a fun book to learn more about bees.

☐ Crowder, Les and Harrell, Heather *Top-Bar Beekeeping, Organic Practices for Honeybee Health.* Good explanations of the differences in top-bar beekeeping.

☐ Delaplane, Keith *First Lessons in Beekeeping.* Nice start to understanding the art, and science, of keeping bees, often used as a reference in beginning beekeeping classes.

☐ Gardiner, Mary *Good Garden Bugs.* Get to know the other garden insects that can help keep your garden stay healthy and keep you away from using pesticides. You will need to stop using these products if you want to successfully keep bees.

☐ Gary, Norman *Honey Bee Hobbyist.* Well-written basic to third year beekeepers geared towards the hobby beekeeper. (2010)

☐ Hubbell, Sue *A Book of Bees and How to Keep Them.* Charming classic book about beekeeping in Missouri in the 1970s.

☐ Lindtner, Peter *Garden Plants for Honeybees.* Good start to identify what plants will feed your bees, includes major nectar and pollen sources by month.

☐ Marchese, C. Marina *Honeybee Lessons from an Accidental Beekeeper.* Interesting story of how her neighbor introduced her to beekeeping, handy recipes and a quick read.

☐ Phillips, Tanya *Beginning Beekeeping.* Great pictures and explanations of the adventure you are about to start, the subtitle is "Everything You Need to Make Your Hive Thrive!"

☐ Riotte, Louise *Carrots Love Tomatoes Updated and Revised.* Get familiar with the concept of companion planting, which is using plant combinations to deter bugs in your garden. It works and will come in handy as you stop using insecticides and pesticides.

☐ Sammataro, Diana and Alphonse Avitabile, *The Beekeeper's Handbook* **Fifth Edition.** Great book you will use for many years, one of the first book you should buy for your beekeeping reference library. Published 2021.

☐ Sanford, Malcolm T. and Richard E. Bonney, *Storey's Guide to Keeping Honey Bees,* 2018. Good photos in this beginning beekeeping guide.

☐ Seeley, Thomas *Honeybee Democracy.* Explains how the colony manages and navigates in a swarm. A little technical in some parts but still a fascinating read.

☐ Seeley, Thomas *The Lives of Bees* compares bees in the wild to current beekeeping practices. Published 2019.

☐ Stewart, Tabori and Chang *The Beekeeper's Bible.* Lovely coffee table book with a wide range of beekeeping-related topics from the history of beekeeping to wax recipes, a perfect Christmas gift. That's how I got my copy!

☐ Traynor, Kirsten *Two Million Blooms.* The definitive book on honey and its medicinal properties, written to outline what is known, and not known, about the effects of honey and its related properties.

☐ Traynor, Kirsten S. and Michael, *Simple Smart Beekeeping,* simple beekeeping book focused on the basics for keeping healthy hives. Published 2015.

☐ Wiggins, Charlotte Ekker, *"Bee Club Basics or How to Start a Bee Club,"* an easy to use non-profit club management guide with a pull out section with monthly discussion topics and other helpful check lists. Published 2019.

☐ Whynott, Douglas *Following the Bloom.* A romp through the lives of migratory commercial beekeepers; informative, eye-opening and sheer fun. Published 2004.

MAGAZINES

☐ **American Bee Journal**, published by Dadant featuring a wide range of beekeeping-related topics.

☐ **Bee Culture Magazine,** published by A.I. Root also features a wide range of beekeeping articles.

Most beekeepers subscribe to both magazines. Also check with your local library. If they don't carry both magazines suggest that they do.

Handy for would be young beekeepers,
*Mattel now has **Beekeeper Barbie***
including her very own hives and bees.

FILMS AND VIDEOS

☐ **The Bee Understanding Project Film:** There are many factors that affect honey bee health. What people can do differently is one of them. This is the story of four people who swapped jobs to learn more about protecting bees. **http://bit.ly/TheBeeProject**

- ☐ Tools for *Varroa* Management including a library of interesting videos from Honeybee Health Coalition: **https://honeybeehealthcoalition.org/varroa**

- ☐ *Varroa* mites in Brood Frame April 2018: **https://bit.ly/Varroamites**

OTHER GOOD ONLINE RESOURCES

- ☐ **Bee Source,** online beekeeping discussion forum. Get a cup of coffee first, you can spend hours surfing through this site. **https://beesource.com**

- ☐ **LEAD for Pollinators,** educational non-profit offering educational and organizational support to beekeepers and the organizations that support them. **https://leadforpollinators.org**

- ☐ **National Honey Board Recipes,** good source for cooking with honey recipes. **https://www.honey.com/recipes**

- ☐ **Pollinator Partnership Ecoregional Planting Guides,** good list of plants for pollinators including honey bees. **https://pollinator.org/guides**

- ☐ **Protecting Pollinators Certified Pesticides Applicators, Pesticides and Crop Advisors and Agricultural Producers Training** (order USB drive at info at pollinator.org) **https://www.pollinator.org/pesticide-education**

- ☐ **Seven Things You Can Do To Help Pollinators** **https://www.pollinator.org/7things**

COMMUNITY AND VOLUNTEER PROJECTS

- ☐ **Bee City USA and Bee Campus USA** program recognizes communities planting and developing sustainable habitats for pollinators sponsored by Xerxes Society. **https://www.beecityusa.org**

- ☐ **HoneyBee Net** provides a central location for the collection and sharing of nectar flow records by volunteers and provides comparisons with satummi data, part of the National Phenology Network. **http://go.nasa.gov/38Uv7Io**

OTHER BOOKS/VIDEOS/RESOURCES

AUTHOR	TITLE	NOTES

Your Notes

CHAPTER 17
Beekeeping Terms

Abdomen: The back side of the honey bee that contains all of the digestive organs and stinger.

Abscond: When bees abandon hive completely or leave just the queen and a few bees. Can occur for a variety of reasons including pressure from pests, excessive heat or water, lack of food and if they are checked/disturbed too frequently when first established in a new hive.

After swarms: Smaller swarms after the colony initially swarms, each with a virgin queen.

Africanized: Aggressive and high producing honey bee colonies descendant from an escaped Brazilian strain.

Age polytheism: Worker bee jobs depending on age.

Alarm pheromone: A volatile, banana-like scent given off by honey bees when they sting and marks the attacker so other bees can identify the source of the threat.

Alcohol Wash: Collecting ½ cup of nurse bees in a jar with alcohol or soapy water for one minute, then poured on a white surface through #8 hardware cloth to count *varroa* mites. Recommended mite levels are no more than 1 mites per 100 bees or 3 mites per 300 bees.

American foulbrood: American foulbrood (AFB) is a fatal bacterial disease of honey bee brood caused by the spore forming bacterium *Paenibacillus larvae*. Uncommon yet most destructive brood disease.

Anaphylaxis: An acute allergic reaction to an antigen like bee venom to which the body has become hypersensitive.

Antennae: Segmented, freely moving from the socket-like head base. Honey bees use their antennae to smell and touch.

Ants: Ants and bees often live together. If ants are found inside the hive, sprinkle the inside cover with fresh ground cinnamon to discourage them.

Apiary: Bee yard with honey bee colonies. Also called bee garden.

Apiculture: Latin-based term for beekeeping.

Apis: Bee in Latin.

Apis mellifera: Latin name for today's honey bee. *Mellifera* in Latin means honey.

Arthropods: Invertebrate animal of the larger phylum Arthropoda that includes insects, spiders and crustaceans.

Bald-faced hornet: (*Dolichovespula maculate*) is a yellow jacket-type of wasp, not a true hornet. It is not yellow/black but black/white. Colonies contain 400 to 700 workers. It builds a characteristic large hanging paper nest and workers aggressively defend their home.

Balling: Worker bees encircle a queen and raise their body temperature until the queen is overheated and dies. Bees will ball their queen when she is old, not laying properly, injured and, at times, when she is a newly-introduced queen or other intruders such as wasps.

Bearding: Bees hanging down from the hive entrance in a beard-like shape, most frequently during hot summer days. Bees hang outside to help cool off the inside of hive.

Beebread: Pollen mixed with enzymes packed in wax cells around brood nest to be fed to larvae and nurse bees. Packed in cells by workers adding nectar and salivary secretions causing fermentation and covered with layer of honey.

Bee Buddy: Someone who is starting their beekeeping adventure at the same time as you are, lives close by and you both can inspect each others hives, share equipment and learn together.

"Bee Haver": Someone who has bees but does not regularly care for them.

Bee Pasture: Planting to attract wild bee populations.

Bee Space: ¼ to ⅜th inch space honey bees will not fill with wax and propolis. Concept first utilized in hive design by Reverend Langstroth in 1852.

Bee Tree: Trees that house bees in their dying, hollow trunks.

Beehive: A structure that houses a colony of honey bees.

Beekeeper: Person dedicated to keeping honey bees healthy and well under their care. Someone gets to call themselves a beekeeper once they help their bees survive a winter.

Beekeeping Etiquette: How to be a good neighbor and a considerate fellow beekeeper.

Beekeeping Lingerie: Jacket made of lightweight netting to keep user safe from bees and other bugs.

Beeswax: Wax honey bees secrete from eight glands on their underside and used to build their combs.

Bottom Board: Beehive floor. May be solid, screened and screened with a removable solid insert.

Bottom Supering: adding honey super boxes above the brood boxes and under already existing honey supers on the hive.

Box: Refers to the super or hive body you select to use; it can be a deep or medium in various widths. Beginning beekeepers sometimes refer to these as "drawers."

Brace Comb: Comb built between combs and the hive.

Brood: Young developing bees found in their wax comb cells varying from egg, larva and pupae.

Brood Box: Hive box with mostly if not all brood, tends to be the bottom one to three hive boxes.

Brood Break: Removing brood to disrupt mites that settle in brood. Also a period of time when queen stops laying for a variety of reasons.

Brood Chamber: Baby bee nursery, usually bottom hive bodies, either one or two deeps or three medium supers.

Brood Frame: A frame with eggs and capped larvae cells.

Brood Nest: Where bees raise baby bees or brood; a collection of frames with brood on them.

Brood Pattern: The typical queen bee laying pattern in the frame center.

Brood Stain: Repeated use of wax comb for egg laying and larval development darkens the wax with excrement and larval cocoons, helps to identify older comb that should be replaced every 2 years or so.

Buckfast: Type of bee breed.

Burr Comb: Wild comb drawn in unwanted spaces.

Bylaws: Rules and regulations designed to manage the actions of a club and organization's members and activities.

Candy Plug: Honey and confectioner's sugar mixed into a putty-like substance that is used to plug a queen cage with queen and retinue inside. Bees eat through the candy plug to release the Queen bee from her cage.

Carniolan: Honey bee race.

Castes: Specialized social animals subsets. In honey bees, reproductive queen bees and non-reproducing female worker bees.

Cell: A single honeycomb compartment where eggs are laid and food is stored.

Checkerboarding: Moving frames up to the next box in an alternating pattern of a drawn frame of comb and an empty one.

Chunk honey: Pieces of comb honey packed in a jar with liquid extracted honey.

Cleansing flight: Bees fly outside the hive to defecate.

Club Charter: Basic operational guidelines for a beginning club that include minimum legal requirements.

Cluster: Bees grouped together in winter to conserve heat, constantly shivering wing muscles to keep queen and bees inside the cluster warm starting at 50F. May also refer to a summertime swarm gathered on a tree or structure.

Colony: A family of honey bees with a laying queen, worker bees and for most of spring and summer, drones.

Colony Collapse Disorder: First used in 2006 to describe massive bee deaths. Today no longer a mystery, it is attributed to the impact of *Varroa* mites.

Comb: Six-sided wax cells built by honey bees where young are raised and food is stored.

Comb Foundation: Beeswax sheets or plastic that form a base for bees to draw wax comb.

Corbicula: Pollen basket on honey bee legs or hairs where bees carry pollen.

Crop: Honey-carrying organ located above the honey bee mid gut. Bees regurgitate nectar to other bees that then store nectar in comb to dehydrate it into honey.

Cut comb honey: Honey squares in the sealed comb as the bees made it packaged in a clear container.

Dead Out: A colony that died inside a hive.

Dearth: A period of time when bee forage is scarce or non-existent.

Deep: also called deep hive body and brood chamber. These boxes are 19⅞ inch-long, 16¼ inch wide and 9⅝ inch high. For 8 frames, the deep is 14 inches wide. When full of honey, a deep 10-frame box may weigh 80 pounds and an 8-frame deep may weight 65 pounds.

Deformed Wing Virus: One of the two dozen viruses carried by *Varroa* mites resulting in deformed honey bee wings.

Drifting: Field bees returning to colonies that aren't their original home.

Double Deep: The use of two deep boxes for the brood chamber, where the queen bee lays eggs and nurse bees raise young bees.

Draw: To shape and build as in to draw wax comb on a frame.

Drone: Male stingless honey bee carrying 50% of a colony's genetics. The main job of the drone is to mate with virgin queen bees from other colonies.

Drone Congregation Area: An area drones visit about ½ mile from their home hive where they patrol in an effort to locate and mate with queens. Queens however, fly farther for mating, around 3 miles. On three to five mating flights queens may mate with 12-20 drones, securing genetic diversity for the mated queen's offspring.

Dysentery: Excess bee feces released inside or near a hive, usually in winter when bees can't get outside. May also be caused by poor nutrition. Sometimes confused with nosema disease.

Eclose: My buddy David's favorite beekeeping term to describe emerging from a pupa. Often used interchangeably with hatch.

Eggs: Tiny rice-like grains the queen lays on cell bottoms.

Emergency Queen Cells: Small queen cells built in the event worker bees need to raise a new queen.

Endophallus: Drone reproductive organ.

EpiPen® Brand name of an auto-injectable device that delivers the drug epinephrine. It is a life-saving medication used when someone is experiencing a severe allergic reaction, known as anaphylaxis.

European foulbrood: Bacteria that infect colony larva and is contagious. EBF is less deadly than American foulbrood and can sometimes be managed.

Eusocial: (*Vespa crabro*) is the largest eusocial wasp native to Europe. It is also the only true hornet found in North America, having been introduced by European settlers in the 1800s.

Extracted honey: Liquid honey removed from a colony.

Extracting: Removing honey from frames either by hand and/or using specialized equipment.

Extractor: Hand-cranked and motorized tanks that hold frames and through centrifugal force remove honey from the frames.

Fat Body: Section of tissue that holds fat cells, as well as glycogen, protein, and high concentrations of mitochondria and enzymes. The fat body is the equivalent in insect terms of a mix of a liver and fat storage and is basically the honey bees immune system. Latest research confirms *Varroa* feeds on a bee's fat body and not its blood.

Festooning: When worker bees form a plumb line by holding on to each other's legs.

Festooning, when worker bees hang on to each other's legs to form a living plumb line that guides them in wax comb production.

Field bee or Forager: An older worker bee at least 4 weeks old that travels out of the hive to collect nectar, pollen, water and propolis.

Fondant: A sugar candy used as emergency winter food.

Forager: A worker bee usually 4 weeks old that leaves the hive in search of nectar, pollen, water or propolis. Also called a field bee.

Foulbrood: General name for infectious diseases affecting brood that cause bee larvae and/or pupae to die.

Foundationless Frames: Frames with starter strips at the top so worker bees can draw comb without a pattern or support. Hive must be level for proper foundationless comb production.

Frame: A wooden or plastic rectangle that either has starter strips at the top or foundation where bees build wax, store food and lay eggs removable from the hive body for inspection and management purposes.

Frass: Black spots and filaments found on comb, frames and bottom boards, excrement of other insects including wax moths and small hive beetles.

Garden Cover: Pitched roof hive cover that is prettier than practical.

Great Plains Master Beekeeping Program: Scientifically vetted and professionally managed educational beekeeping certification program from University of Nebraska at Lincoln.

Grafting: Moving a newly hatched worker larvae into a special queen cell to raise a new queen.

Granulate: When honey bee crystalizes. To re-liquefy, place the closed glass jar in a warm water bath.

Guard bees: Worker bees that patrol the entrance ready to attack unwanted intruders. They often part their wings before they fly up to attack.

Hatch: To come out of an egg. Break open and come forth. Bees eclose or emerge from the pupal case.

Hemolymph: Insect blood.

Herbicide: A substance that is toxic to plants, used to destroy unwanted vegetation.

Hive: As a verb, to put a swarm in a hive. A hive is a man-made home for honey bees. As a noun, it refers to the bee's home.

Hive Body: Single wooden box or shell that holds frames.

Hive Carrier: Metal brace that easily lifts a hive so that it can be safely carried.

Hive Cover: Hive roof or removable top.

Hive Stand: A structure that keeps hive off the ground.

Hive Tool: Metal tool to pry hive lid and frames, often misplaced.

Honeycomb: Six-sided wax cells build by honey bees where young are raised and food is stored.

Honeydew: A sticky sugar-rich liquid secreted by insects as they fee on plant sap.

Honey Bee: Two words referring to *Apis mellifera (Latin)*

Honey Bound: When colonies store too much nectar so that the queen has no room to lay. Often triggers swarming.

Honey Crop: The storage stomach honey bees use to transport nectar and water. Has a one-way valve, keeping the contents separate from the rest of the digestive tract.

Honey Dipper: Kitchen utensil used to collect viscous liquid like honey from a container, which it then exudes to another location such as a bread roll. Usually made of turned wood.

Honey Flow: Misnomer, more correctly "nectar flow," when plants are producing nectar to attract bees and other pollinators to move pollen from one plant to the next so the plants reproduce.

House Bee: Young worker bee one day to two weeks old that works only inside the hive.

Hygienic Behavior: A heritable trait of individual workers that confers colony-level resistance against various brood diseases. Hygienic workers detect and remove dead or diseased brood from sealed cells.

Hypopharyngeal Gland: Twin glands in worker bee heads used to produce larvae food. Bees activate these food glands by consuming pollen. They shrink as a bee transitions to foraging.

"Illinois:" Refers to a medium super of either 8 or 10 frames. Named for an Illinois beekeeping company that developed the 19⅞-inch long, 16¼-inch wide and 6⅝-inch high hive box.

Imirie Shim® is a gadget developed by George Imirie, a well-known Northeast beekeeper. It is a simple ¾-inch rectangular frame that is the same size (width and length) as a honey super. The shim has a ¾-inch notch cut ⅜-inch deep in the middle of the frontend bars. The shim can be placed between any of the honey supers to allow for additional access for foraging bees. Since the shim also provides additional ventilation, you can place it on top of (or under) the inner cove to allow a place for moisture to leave the hive.

Indicator Species: Much like a canary in a coal mine, indicator species are a barometer of the overall health of an interdependent ecosystem.

Inner Cover: Thin wooden board placed beneath the hive cover.

Insecticides: A substance used for killing insects.

Instrumental Insemination: Artificially inseminating a honey bee queen using a small stand that holds the queen in place.

Italian: Honey bee race.

Keystone Species: A species on which other species in an ecosystem largely depend, such that if it were removed the ecosystem would change drastically.

Kitchen towels: Made out of non-sticky muslin, excellent to cover open hive boxes to keep bees calm. Also handy for beekeeper to absorb neck sweat and can be used as a head band.

Langstroth hive: A hive with movable frames named after Reverend L. L. Langstroth.

Larva: Grub-like immature honey bee. Plural larvae.

Laying worker: A worker bee that no longer is exposed to brood and/or a queen pheromone and starts laying unfertilized eggs.

Mandibles: Honey bee mouthparts.

Marked queen: A queen bee with a dab of paint on her thorax color coordinated by year so beekeepers can easily find her in the hive.

Mating Flight: When a virgin queen flies out to mate; typically mating with 15-20 drones. Queens may go on 1-3 separate mating flights.

Mead: Alcoholic beverage created by fermenting honey with water, sometimes with various fruits, spices, grains, or hops. The alcoholic content ranges from about 3.5% ABV to more than 20%.

Medium: Refers to a hive body box with 10 frames that is 19⅞-inch long, 16¼ inch wide and 6⅝ inch high. For 8-frames, medium boxes are 14 inches wide. When full of honey, a 10-frame medium may weigh 50 pounds and an 8-frame medium may weigh 40 pounds.

Metamorphosis: Changes an insect makes as it moves from egg to larvae to pupa, then adult.

Microbial Meat: Beneficial bacteria and fungi naturally occurring in pollen. Bees need these non-plant proteins to complete their growth and development. They increase pollen's nutritional value by adding amino acids, protein's building blocks, that flowering plants alone may not always provide.

Migratory Beekeeping: Moving colonies from one area to the next to take advantage of different honey flows and for crop pollination.

Migratory Cover: A cover which is same width as hive body with extensions extending down only on front and back. Does not require inner cover.

Minnesota Hygienic: Bee breed developed by Marla Spivek in 1980s with enhanced resistance to *Varroa* mites.

Mono Floral Honey: A type of honey which has a distinct flavor or other attribute due to its being predominantly from the nectar of one plant species. Does not provide bees with all of the vitamins, minerals and amino acids bees need to remain healthy.

Mouse Guard: Metal or mesh guard placed over the hive entrance to keep mice from getting into the hive(s).

Movable Frame: A comb frame that can be easily removed from a hive.

Multi Floral Honey: Commonly referred to as "wildflower" honey from a variety of different flowers and nectar sources.

Nasonov Gland: A gland that issues a lemon-like pheromone that guides and recruits worker bees.

Native Bees: Local bees that are dependent on local food sources, such as mason bees, leaf cutter bees.

Nectar: Sweet liquid plants secrete to attract pollinators. Bees dehydrate it to 16-18% to make it honey.

Nectar Flow: When bees are collecting nectar and building comb. Plants produce nectar when temperatures range from 74°F to 86°F.

Newspaper Unite or Unite: Merging hives using a newspaper with tiny slits placed in between two supers.

Nosema: Adult honey bee mid-gut or stomach infectious disease. Symptoms closely resemble those of dysentery.

Nuc: Small starter colony containing a laying queen and several frames of brood in all stages of development along with honey and pollen.

Nurse Bees: Young worker bees typically 3-14 days old that provide brood food to developing larvae and feed the queen.

Observation Hive: A hive where bees can be seen without being disturbed.

Old Comb: Reused wax comb that absorbs pesticide residue bees carry in from the outside. Should be replaced every three years.

Open Feed: Providing honey bees food outside the hive.

Orientation Flight: First worker bee flights as they transition from in-hive jobs to outside foraging, usually figure eight flights in hive front.

Out Yard: Apiary away from beekeeper's home bee garden.

Ovary: Female reproductive tissue responsible for egg production. Queen ovaries typically consist of 200+ individual strands called ovarioles.

Overwinter: When an organism survives winter and regenerates in the next spring growing season.

Oxalic Acid: A natural compound used in vapor and syrup form to manage *Varroa* mite levels.

Package Bees: A queen bee and 2-4 pounds of honey bees in a screened in box with a can of sugar syrup for food.

Paper Wasps: Vespid wasps that gather dead wood and plant fibers, which they mix with saliva, and use to construct water-resistant nests made of gray and brown papery material.

Para Moth™: *Para*-dichlorobenzine. Specific dry crystals used to control mast moths in stored supers. Different from moth balls.

Pesticides: General name for products used to kill undesirables from insects, plants and animals.

Phenology: Monitoring cyclical and seasonal natural phenomena, especially in relation to climate and plant and animal life.

Pheromones: Chemical signals with effects on members of the same species, either creating an immediate behavioral response or a longer term physiological change.

Phoretic: Biological term to describe an association between two species where one transports the other. In honey bees, most often used to describe flightless *Varroa* mites moving from bee to bee.

Pollen: The male reproductive cells of plants collected by bees as protein for young bee food.

Pollen Basket: Special hairs on the back of worker bee legs used to transport pollen back to the hive. Also called corbicula.

Pollen Substitute: Water, sugar, soy flour and other ingredients used as early spring bee food before temperatures are warm enough to trigger nectar flow. Normally shaped into a patty and dough like substance.

Plumrose hair: The branched type of body hair found in bees, which is adapted to pick up and retain pollen grains when a bee brushes against the anthers (male parts) of flowers.

Proboscis: Honey bee tongue.

Propolis: Tree resins mixed with enzymes, the equivalent of bee glue used to seal up hive openings, seal supers and provide anti-bacterial colony protection.

Pupa: Brood phase between larva and adult. Normally cannot be seen but is represented in hive as "capped brood". Plural pupae.

Queen: Sexually developed female honey bee, the mother of the bee colony.

Queen Begonia: The name of the queen bee on the front of this series of illustrated beekeeping books.

Queen Cage: Small containers that temporarily house a queen bee and sometimes a small retinue during transportation.

Queen Cell: Worker bees raising a new queen. Depending on where the queen cell is being raised, it indicates bees preparing to swarm or to raise a new queen bee to supersede the current queen bee.

Queen Cups: Empty cups worker bees build in case they need somewhere to raise a queen bee.

Queen Excluder: A grill device large enough for worker bees to move through but not the queen.

Queen Mandibular Pheromone: A multicomponent pheromone released by the queen that impacts colony dynamics including stimulating retinue behavior and helping to suppress worker reproduction.

Queen Right: When a functioning colony has a mated queen producing eggs.

Rendering: Melting old comb and wax caps to refine beeswax for reuse.

Re-Queen: Replacing old queen with a new queen bee.

Retinue: A circle of attendant worker bees that groom and feed the queen.

Reversing Hive Bodies: The practice of reversing hive bodies in early spring to move the bottom empty box to the top of the second box allowing the queen space to expand.

Robber Bee: Field honey bees from a strong colony taking honey from another colony.

Robbing: Non-colony bees moving into a colony and stealing existing hive resources.

Rolling the Queen: Killing a queen as a frame is removed quickly from a hive.

Round Dance: Circular dance that indicates close food source.

Royal Jelly: White, gelatinous food produced by young worker bees and fed to developing queens and the first few days of a worker bee and drone development. Also called bee milk.

Running Your Hives: Managing your hives.

Scout Bees: Bees that seek out food sources and nest sites after a colony swarmed.

Screened Inner Cover: Inner cover covered in screen to allow increased ventilation.

Sealed (also Capped) Brood: Pupae stage honey bees sealed in wax comb cells.

Shallow: Supers used just for honey collecting; not much used any more. They are $19\frac{7}{8}$ inch long, $16\frac{1}{4}$ inch wide and $5\frac{11}{16}$ inch high.

Sickle Dance: Is performed when the resource is located between 10 to 100 meters. The bee dances similar to the round dance except with several crescent shaped formations on the comb.

Skep: Basket-shaped hives used to keep bees. The colonies had to be destroyed to remove the honey. Not used in the US because most states require removable frames.

Small Hive Beetles: *(Aethina tumida)* Sub-Saharan Africa invasive that takes over hives when colony generates a stress pheromone. Resembles a tiny black ladybug. Winters over inside the hive in the bee cluster. Tricks nurse bees into feeding them.

Smoker: A metallic can holds burning fuels to generate cool smoke to keep honey bees calm by masking the alarm pheromone. Hot smoke burns honey bee wings and antennae.

Smoker Chimney: Where the smoke comes out of the smoker.

Smoker Tray: A small tray that fits inside the smoker at the bottom with holes to allow air to be pushed through with bellows.

Sonication: Also called buzz pollination. Bumblebees grasp flowers and vibrate flight muscles to remove pollen.

Sticky Board: $\frac{1}{8}$th inch thick, white corrugated plastic. Some have a graph printed on them so that counting *varroa* mites is easier. Sticky boards cannot be used with a solid bottom board; the bottom board has to be screened.

Sting: Body part of a bee that injects a venom. Also a reference to what a bee does when injecting the venom.

Stress: Adverse bee impacts including poor nutrition, environmental contamination, improper management and pests and diseases.

Solar Wax Extractor: Glass-covered box for melting beeswax with sunlight.

Spermatheca: Queen bee's sperm storage organ.

Split: Dividing a colony into two or more colonies by adding a queen bee or allowing bees to raise one.

Sugar Shake: Shake ½ cup of nurse bees into a jar with #8 hardware cloth on the lid. Add 1-2 tablespoons powdered sugar and gently shake for 2 minutes. Shake sugar out on a white surface and count *Varroa* mites. Mite levels more than 1 per 100 bees or 3 mites per 300 bees require management.

Super: Hive body used for honey storage above the brood chamber.

Superorganism: Group of organisms of the same species synergetically interacting.

Supersedure Cell: A queen cell being built usually in the middle of the frame to grow a new queen to take over from the existing queen bee.

Swarm: Usually old queen and ⅓ to ½ of an established colony leave to set up house elsewhere. Swarms are a colony's natural instinct to reproduce.

Swarm Cells: Worker bees growing new queens in preparation for swarming, usually found on the bottom and lower part of the frames.

Telescoping Cover: A hive cover that extends downward for several inches on all four hive sides. Requires use of an inner cover.

Telling the Bees: Tradition that started in Germany to include telling the bees of major life events including weddings and the beekeeper's death.

Temporal Polyethism: How bees move through tasks as they age.

Thorax: The round central part of a honey bee body that accommodates the wings and legs. Young worker bees have hairs on their thorax while older bees have a smoother, shinier thorax.

Timing: Executing at the optimum time for the colony.

Top Bar Hive: Horizontally oriented hive that uses wide bars instead of movable frames where bees draw wild natural comb.

Trophallactic Behavior: Exhibiting the exchange of regurgitated food that occurs between adults and larvae in colonies of social insects. Pest species can mimic this behavior (i.e., small hive beetle) with their antennae in order to induce regurgitation of honey from nurse bees.

Two to One: Reference to the sugar to water ratio to make sugar syrup to feed bees. The first number refers to the sugar, the second number to the water.

Uniting: Combining hives.

Varroa: (*Varroa destructor*) invasive mite that carries viruses that, unmanaged, can decimate colonies in their 2nd and 3rd years.

Veil: Protective garment beekeepers wear to shield their face while inspecting hives.

Virgin Queen: Unmated queen.

Waggle Dance: Term used in beekeeping and ethology for a particular figure-eight dance of the honey bee that communicates distance and food source direction located by foraging bees.

Walk Away Split: Dividing a colony by splitting resources and allowing colony without a queen to raise its own queen.

Wax Comb Cappings: The top wax of sealed honey frames when honey is being extracted.

Wax Glands: Abdominal worker bee glands that produce small, translucent white platelets of new beeswax.

Wax Moths: Opportunistic moths that take over weakening and weak colonies and consume comb, pollen and honey bee pupae leaving weblike filaments with excrement on frames and larvae cocoons on hive body sides and frames.

Windbreaks: Hive protection from strong directional winds such as straw bales.

Wiring: Installing a wire in frames to support comb weight.

Wired Foundation: Comb foundation with vertical and horizontal support wires.

Wonky Comb: Wild uneven comb built on wax deficient foundation.

Worker Bee: Female honey bee, the mainstay of any managed honey bee colony.

Worker Cell: Standard beeswax cells used to hold developing worker larvae, honey and pollen stores. Smaller than drone cells.

Yellow Jackets: Carnivorous honey bee wasp cousins the same size as honey bees and often mistaken for honey bees late in the summer season. Ground-nesters.

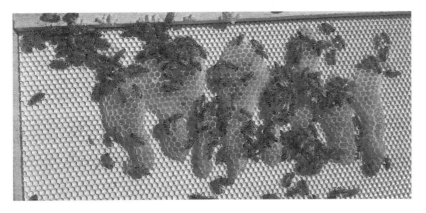

GOOD TO KNOW
TIP

*I use my term, **wonky comb,** for wax comb built in inconvenient places to the beekeeper. Too much space between frames and lack of wax on the frame contribute to this kind of comb-building.*

Your Notes

_____

_____

_____

_____

_____

_____

_____

_____

_____

Your Notes

About the Author

Charlotte Ekker Wiggins in Bluebird Gardens, her one-acre Missouri hillside garden, Monarch Way Station, certified wildlife refuge and apiary.

When she first decided to keep honey bees, Charlotte was like many beginning beekeepers "scared to death." She wanted bees for pollination. Her initial plan was to settle hives in a back garden corner and "coexist." She didn't count on falling in love.

Honey bees "are the most amazing little creatures and part of the tiny bug world that forms the foundation of our interdependent ecosystems." Their declining numbers, what that means to the world's food supply and what we can all do to help them was the topic of her Missouri S&T TEDx April 11, 2019 **"Beekeeping; Why Bugs Matter."** **bit.ly/WhyBugsMatter**

Charlotte began teaching beginning beekeeping in 2012 at the request of her local Extension Office. In 2014, students from one of her beginning beekeeping classes asked for a local club to support them and the Rolla Bee Club was started. In 2019, **Rolla Bee Club** officially became an educational non-profit.

Charlotte has a **master's degree in management** from Webster University, St. Louis. She's founded more than a dozen educational non-profits since 1979 including a humane society, public relations clubs and, most recently, a bee club.

During her public affairs careers in the US Navy and US Forest Service, she spent two decades developing and giving a variety of classes. She is also a contributing author and master gardener representative on **Missouri's Master Pollinator Steward Program Steering Committee,** developed under the University of Missouri College of Natural Resources. The award-winning program, started in 2016 and launched in 2019, is designed to teach the general public about the value of pollinators and what they can do to help them. **bit.ly/3g9SSho**

*"Giving my bee buddy David Draker a bottle of wine from one of our beekeeping students right after it was announced October 10, 2020 that he was selected **Missouri State Beekeeper Association's 2020 Mentor of the Year.** Congratulations again, David, so well deserved!"*

In 2015, Charlotte was awarded a **Missouri State Beekeepers Association Beekeeper of the Year** award along with a team of other volunteers who changed Missouri's honey labeling laws.

September 2022, Charlotte and one other Missouri beekeeper became the first Great Plains Master Beekeeping Program Certified Master Beekeepers. The two are also Missouri's first certified master beekeepers.

Charlotte lives with rescue cats on a one-acre Missouri limestone hillside garden. The garden is a certified wildlife habitat, Monarch Way Station, and apiary that inspires her custom gift business **Bluebird Gardens.**

Charlotte frequently lectures on planting for pollinators and how to start a bee club. For more details, check **charlotteekkerwiggins.com.**

*Charlotte talked about "Why Bugs Matter" April 11, 2019 at Missouri S&T's TEDx. She has applied the principles **she recommended in her one-acre limestone hillside garden and apiary.***

OTHER PUBLISHED WORKS:

Bee Club Basics: How to Start a Bee Club *is a guide to establishing an educational non-profit club. The guide includes a variety of guides, suggested monthly programs, planning check lists and other helpful information. The guide is approved for Great Plains Master Beekeeping program certification credit.*

Available at **Bluebird Gardens.com**:

Bee Clubs Basic Book: **bit.ly/BeeClubBasics**

Bee Club Basics Gift Kit: **bit.ly/BeeGiftKit**

Also available on Amazon:
https://amzn.to/3mzj3Qo

 **LOOK FOR THIS UPDATED VERSION** *Available 2022*

COMING NEXT:

Bees Need Flowers: Planting for Pollinators

Learn how to start and improve your garden so that your bees and other pollinators are getting the nutritious food they need. In turn, your garden produces higher yields because of resident pollinators. It's a win-win!

Available Spring 2023

SIGN UP FOR CHARLOTTE'S WEEKLY GARDEN NOTES

Sign up for Charlotte's weekly free **Garden Notes** highlighting USDA Hardiness zone 5b/6a gardening, beekeeping, cooking and easy home décor tips: **bit.ly/BBG_Subscribe**

CHARLOTTE'S BLOGS

Charlotte also frequently blogs at these sites:

- **http://www.GardeningCharlotte.com**, tips on Missouri gardening.
- **http://www.HomeSweetBees.com**, beekeeping in Missouri buzz.
- **http://www.ATeaspoon.com**, food facts and easy recipe favorites.
- **http://www.MadeJustForU.com,** personalized quilts, gifts and easy home décor ideas.

For more writing samples, visit: **www.charlotteekkerwiggins.com/writing-samples.html**

Sources

A

Art, Scott, *"When is pollinating almonds actually profitable for beekeepers?"* American Bee Journal, December 2019.

B

Bartomeus, Ignasi et al, *"Contribution of insect pollinators to crop yield and quality varies with agricultural intensification,"* US National Library of Medicine, National Institute of Health, March 27, 2014.

Bean, Karen E. *"What happens to honeybees in winter,"* Brookfield Farm Bee and Honey Blog, November 2010.

Bee Base UK: **https://bit.ly/2Yu8ZoX**

Bee Informed Partnership: **https://beeinformed.org**

Bee Source Beekeeping Forums: **https://www.beesource.com/forums/**

Bee Facts: **http://bit.ly/BeeFactsTrivia**

Bonney, Richard E., *"Hive Management, A Seasonal Guide for Beekeepers,"* 1990.

Borba, Renata and Marla Spivak, *"Propolis envelope in Apis mellifera colonies supports honey bees against the pathogen, Paenibacillus larvae,"* Scientific Reports, September 2017.

Bremness, Lesley, *"The Complete Book of Herbs,"* 1988.

C

Canadian Agriculture and Food Museum: **https://bit.ly/2L4pygY**

Caron, Dewey M. and Lawrence John Connor, *"Honey Bee Biology and Beekeeping,"* 2013.

Connor, Lawrence John, *"Bee-sentials A Field Guide,"* 2012.

Chubak, Albert, *"The Honor of Being a Mentor,"* American Beekeeping Federation Quarterly, November 2019.

D

Disselkoen, Mel, *"OTS Queen Rearing, A Survival Guide for Beekeepers Worldwide,"* 2016.

G

Garden Fork, Essential oil recipe.
http://www.gardenfork.tv/essential-oil-recipe-for-honeybees.

Great Plains Master Beekeeping Program, University of Nebraska, Lincoln.
https://gpmb.unl.edu

H

Hayes, Jerry, *"Impacts on Today's Honey Bees,"* Missouri State Beekeepers Association Fall Conference October 19, 2018, Kirksville, Mo.

Horn, Tammy, *"Bees in America, How the Honeybee Shaped a Nation,"* 2006.

Hymenopters Genome Database, University of Missouri, BeeBase 2019.

J

Jabr, Ferris, *"Mind-Boggling Math of Migratory Beekeeping,"* Scientific American, September 2013.

K

Kaplan, Kim, *"Deformed Wing Virus Genetic Diversity in US Honey Bees Complicates Search for Remedies,"* American Bee Journal, October 2019.

Kelley, Walter T., *"How to Keep Bees and Sell Honey,"* 1993.

Kemp, Bill, *"The Life Cycle of Osmia Lignaria: Implications for Reading Populations,"* USDA Agricultural Research Service, April 2004.

Kingham, Graham, "Honey Bee Drones" February 2020.

M

Master Gardener Core Course Manual, University of Missouri. 2010.

Mayo Clinic, Rochester, Minnesota.

Miller, Zach et al, *"Conserving Missouri's Wild and Managed Pollinators,"* University of Missouri Extension, August 2018.

Missouri Department of Conservation.

Missouri State Beekeepers Association Best Management Practices: **bit.ly/3oATLBZ**

N

National Geographic, "Honey in Pyramids," November 25, 2015.

National Geographic Kids, "Ten Facts About Honey Bees" **http://bit.ly/3pAossh**

National Honey Board Recipes: **https://honey.com/recipes**

Navarrete-Tindall, Nadia, *"Native Plants for Native Pollinators,"* Lincoln University Cooperative Extension flyer.

P

Phillips, Tanya, *"Beginning Beekeeping"* 2017.

Pilati, Luciano and Paolo Fontana, *"Sequencing the Movement of Honey Bee Colonies between the Forage Sites with the Microeconomic Model of the Migratory Beekeeper,"* Published November 5, 2018.

Pollinator.org: region specific planting guides. **https://www.pollinator.org**

R

Ramsey, Samuel et al, *"Varroa destructor feeds primarily on honey bee fat body tissue and not hemolymph"* January 29, 2019. Proceedings of the National Academy of Science in US.

Robertson, Hugh and Kevin W. Warner, *"Honeybee Chemoreceptors Found for Smell and Taste,"* University of Illinois Champaign-Urbana, 2006.

S

Simone-Finstom, Michael et al, *"Migratory Management and Environmental Conditions Affect Life Span and Oxidative Stress in Honey Bees,"* US National Library of Medicine, National Institute of Health, August 24, 2016.

Smith, Chad, *"Seed Production; Same But Different"* Ag Update, November 8, 2017.

Seeley, Tom, *"The Lives of Bees,"* 2019.

Seeley, Tom, *"The Wisdom of the Hive,"* 1996.

Spevak, Ed, director St. Louis Zoo WildCare Institute and Center for Native Pollination Conservation. *"Honeybees v. Native Bees,"* Missourians for Monarchs October 28, 2019 St. Louis, Mo.

Stein, Katharina et al, *"Bee pollination increases yield quantity and quality of cash crops in Burkina Faso, West Africa."* Scientific Reports, December 18, 2017.

Suszkiw, Jan, *"Microbes on the Menu for Bee Larvae,"* American Bee Journal, October 2019.

T

Tew, James, Catching Swarms, Missouri State Beekeepers Association Spring Conference March 3, 2018, Warrensburg, Mo.

The Kitchen: **https://bit.ly/2MHEBxL**

Traynor, Kirsten, *"Two Million Blossoms, Discovering the Medicinal Benefits of Honey,"* 2011.

Traynor, Kirsten and Michael J. Traynor, *"Simple, Smart Beekeeping,"* 2015.

SOURCES

U

University of Georgia Honey Bee Program, Establishing a Bee Pasture.

Urban Dictionary.

Utah County Beekeepers: **http://www.utahcountybeekeepers.org/fun_facts.html**

USDA Agricultural Services, Pollinating Insects, June 2018.

V

Vandeloecht, Brent, Missouri Department of Conservation, Chairman of the Collaborative Group, Missourians for Monarchs, Missourians for Monarchs Annual Meeting, Belle, Mo. September 11, 2019.

Vance, Joel, *"War Was Never So Sweet,"* Missouri Conservationist October 2010.

W

Wikipedia

Winston, Mark L., *"The Biology of the Honey Bee"* Harvard University Press 1987.

White, Bill, *"The Plight of the Pollinator,"* Missouri Conservationist Magazine January 19, 2016.

White, George O., Missouri State Nursery Seedling Catalog 2019-2020.

Wiggins, Charlotte et al, *"Honey Bees and Pollinators, Their Habitats and Products,"* University of Missouri Extension, Missouri Master Pollinator Steward Program, September 2018.

Your Notes

_____

_____

_____

_____

_____

_____

_____

_____

_____

Index

W

Y

Made in the USA
Las Vegas, NV
25 April 2024

89122587R00171